"For a little thing, you put up quite a fight!"

Adam laughed, catching hold of Lisa's wrists in one hand while his other hand trailed along her face. "Don't you?"

Lisa couldn't answer him. She was too aware of the hard, electrifying warmth of his body against her own. His fingers caressingly probed the hollow at the base of her throat where a pulse throbbed, betraying her.

"Please, Mr. Vandeleur, don't," she begged.

"It will be painless, I assure you," he replied mockingly. "Kissing can be quite an enjoyable pastime when it's done correctly."

"I don't doubt your expertise," she retorted, "but I don't fancy being the recipient under the circumstances."

"You said that very prettily," he laughed softly and dangerously, "but the time for talking is over...."

YVONNE WHITTAL
is also the author of these

Harlequin Romances

1915—EAST TO BARRYVALE
2002—THE SLENDER THREAD
2077—DEVIL'S GATEWAY
2101—WHERE SEAGULLS CRY
2128—PRICE OF HAPPINESS
2162—HANDFUL OF STARDUST
2198—SCARS OF YESTERDAY
2243—MAGIC OF THE BAOBAB
2249—LOVE IS ETERNAL
2304—BITTER ENCHANTMENT
2358—THE MAN FROM AMAZIBU BAY

and this

Harlequin Presents

318—THE BROKEN LINK

Many of these titles are available at your local bookseller.

For a free catalogue listing all available Harlequin Romances
and Harlequin Presents, send your name and address to:

HARLEQUIN READER SERVICE
M.P.O. Box 707, Niagara Falls, NY 14302
Canadian address: Stratford, Ontario N5A 6W2

Summer of the Weeping Rain

by

YVONNE WHITTAL

Harlequin Books

TORONTO • LONDON • LOS ANGELES • AMSTERDAM
SYDNEY • HAMBURG • PARIS • STOCKHOLM • ATHENS • TOKYO

Original hardcover edition published in 1979
by Mills & Boon Limited

ISBN 0-373-02412-6

Harlequin edition published June 1981

CHAPTER ONE

GALE force winds rattled the lounge windows of the small, inexpensive flat Lisa Moreau shared with her mother, and in the narrow street below people walked with their heads bent and their shoulders hunched as they fought against the elements of nature. The sky looked bleak, and Table Mountain was shrouded in a billowing mist that looked every bit as angry as the sea. It had been a bad year for tourists visiting Cape Town, for the weather had been more unpredictable than usual. The winter rains had started early, and the stormy seas had ravaged the coast until this important South African port had lived up to the name given to it by the early Portuguese navigators, 'The Cape Of Storms'. Now, with August almost at an end and spring in the offing, there was still no reprieve from the weather.

Lisa's faintly disconsolate glance turned from the dismal scene outside to the two women seated on the old, floral covered sofa, and she wondered, not for the first time that afternoon, why her mother's sister had chosen to pay them a visit on a day like this when it would have been more sensible to remain indoors.

Molly Anstey was the headmistress at the school where Lisa had been a teacher for the past two and a half years, and it was obvious to Lisa that her aunt had something on her mind; something which Lisa had guessed at from the moment her aunt had stepped into their neat little flat, and something which she shrank from instinctively.

Since the accident which had disrupted Lisa's life during the second school term of that year, she had known that she would inevitably have to face the future again, but now, three months later, she still lacked the courage and the strength to do so.

Lisa sighed inwardly and, leaning heavily on her walking stick, she sat down in a chair facing the two women to observe them in silence while they talked, but she took in nothing of what was being said. Her aunt was still remarkably slender for a woman in her late forties, and showed no sign, as yet, of greying, whereas Lisa's mother, two years older than Molly, was greying swiftly at the temples and slightly plumper than her elegantly clad sister.

Molly Anstey looked up suddenly and met Lisa's direct gaze. For a moment her face was expressionless, then her lips tightened in a manner Lisa knew only too well, and it sent a shiver of apprehension up her spine. Her aunt placed her empty tea-cup in the tray with great care as if it had been made of delicate china and not just cheap imitation, then those slender, capable hands were folded neatly in her lap, and Lisa knew that the dreaded moment had come.

'I want to talk to you very seriously, Lisa, and I'm hoping that you won't think that I'm trying to force you into something you don't want to do, but——' She paused significantly and exchanged a swift glance with Lisa's mother before continuing. 'You need to get away, my dear, for a few months at least, and a stay in the country should be just the thing for you.'

'Are you, in a very polite way, asking me to resign my post at the school, Aunt Molly?' Lisa wanted to know, and her usually soft, pleasant voice was tinged with a sarcasm which had resulted from the recent months of pain, suffering and disillusionment.

'No, my dear,' her aunt contradicted smoothly. 'I'm not asking you to resign if you don't want to, but your mother and I are both fully aware of your reluctance to return to the school after—after——'

'After the accident,' Lisa supplied calmly as her aunt stumbled to an uncomfortable halt.

'Yes,' Molly nodded, recovering herself swiftly. 'Why not go away for a while, Lisa? It would give you the opportunity to get over this whole tragic business.'

'I can't afford an extended holiday, and I dread the thought of being idle,' Lisa said tritely.

'No one suggested that you should remain idle, my dear,' Molly protested hastily. 'Of course you *must* find something to occupy yourself with.'

Lisa's lips curved into a semblance of a smile, but there was also a hint of cynicism in it. 'Jobs are scarce these days, even in the country, and I——'

'As a matter of fact I *do* know of something which might interest you,' her aunt interrupted quickly, and she leaned forward in her seat with a slight urgency to explain. 'An old friend of mine, Erica Vandeleur, recently lost her youngest son and his wife in a plane accident, and she now finds herself looking after their two small children, a boy and a girl aged five.'

'Twins?' Lisa questioned, instantly on the alert.

'Yes,' Molly confirmed. 'Erica lives with her eldest son, Adam, on his sheep farm in the Beaufort West district, and although she finds the children adorable, she hasn't been too well lately, and she realises she's incapable of managing them on her own at the moment. It was Adam, the children's uncle and guardian, who decided that they needed help, and when I received Erica's letter yesterday, asking whether I could recommend someone suitable, I thought instantly of you.'

'Oh, no!' Lisa exclaimed distastefully. 'No, I couldn't!'

'But you're extraordinarily good with children, and it

would be such a wonderful opportunity for you to have a paying holiday in the country,' her aunt argued strongly.

'I'm a teacher, Aunt Molly, not a nursemaid.'

'It would only be for a couple of weeks.'

'A couple of weeks?'

Lisa stared at her incredulously and Molly Anstey shifted uncomfortably in her chair as she confessed, 'Well, a little more than four months, actually, until the children go to boarding school.'

'It's out of the question!' Lisa stated flatly.

'Lisa, my dear, you should at least consider it,' her mother interrupted calmly for the first time. 'You know you've been dreading the idea of going back to the school.'

'And think of all that lovely fresh Karoo air,' Molly added persuasively.

'The summers in the Karoo are hot and dusty, and the winters cold and frosty,' Lisa said sharply and dispassionately, rejecting the idea with every fibre of her being. 'No, thank you, Aunt Molly. I'm a city girl, born and bred, and living on a primitive farm in the Karoo just doesn't appeal to me one bit. I sympathise with Mrs Van—Van—whatever her name is, and I'm sorry for the children, but——'

'Lisa!'

'I'm sorry, Mother,' Lisa turned to the woman who had spoken her name so reprovingly. 'I know you're both trying your best to help me, and I appreciate it, but——'

'It wouldn't be for ever, dear,' her mother interrupted gently, but Lisa shook her fair head adamantly.

'You've got the weekend to think it over, Lisa,' her aunt remarked after a lengthy, tense silence had prevailed in the room. 'Let me know on Monday what you've decided.'

Long after Molly Anstey had left, Lisa remained seated in her chair, her fingers absently fingering the carved handle of the walking stick she wished she could do without. She could hear her mother in the kitchen, rinsing the tea-cups and packing them away, but Lisa's thoughts had gone back in time to that fateful day when her own car had been in for a service and she had accepted a lift to school with her closest friend, Sandy Duncan.

The traffic had been exceptionally heavy that morning, and they had been discussing their plans for the coming winter holidays as well as Lisa's approaching marriage to Rory Phillips. Neither of them had seen the small delivery van jump the red light at a busy intersection until it was on top of them, and then it had been too late to avoid a collision. Lisa could still hear the horrifying crunch of metal and splintering glass on impact, and then she had mercifully known nothing more until she had woken up in hospital several hours later. She had urgently questioned the hospital staff for news of her friend, but they had remained evasive, and it was her mother who had eventually broken it to her that Sandy Duncan had been killed instantly.

The shock of Sandy's death had minimised Lisa's own injuries to unimportance, but they had been brought sharply into focus when Rory, her fiancé, was finally allowed to see her in hospital. With her arm in plaster, her fractured ribs making breathing difficult, and her hip in traction, Lisa had known that she did not look her best, but when Rory stood rigidly at the foot of her bed, she knew that the injuries to her face had been far worse than they had led her to believe. She could have taken his sympathy, his compassion, and even his pity, but the look of horror and revulsion on his lean, handsome features had struck the final blow.

She had somehow wrenched his ring from her swollen finger, and he had accepted it from her without protest before he walked out of the ward, and out of her life. There had been no tears after his departure, only a deadly numbness that left her devoid of feelings, but it was after that incident that she had insisted on having a mirror placed at her disposal, and the face that had confronted her had filled her with self-disgust. Her hair had been cut away just above the left temple where a light gauze dressing covered the stitches she had received there, but it was the long, ugly gash running along the side of her jaw that had upset her most, and her face, puffed and bruised with the minor lacerations she had received, made the sight of her own reflection even more hideous. That was when she had begun to understand the reason for Rory's revulsion, but it did not prevent the bitterness and the contempt she had begun to feel towards the man who had professed to love her so deeply.

'Lisa.' A comforting hand touched her shoulder lightly, jerking her back to the present to discover that she was shaking uncontrollably, and her entire body felt cold and clammy with perspiration. 'Why don't you have a rest before dinner?' her mother suggested with sympathetic understanding. 'I'll give you a call when it's ready.'

'Thank you, Mother,' Lisa smiled up at her wearily and, leaning heavily on her walking stick for moral as well as physical support, she limped across the room and down the short passage to her bedroom.

Reliving the accident, and the events directly following it, had exhausted Lisa, and when her head touched the pillow she slipped into a deep and dreamless sleep from which her mother had difficulty in waking her some two hours later.

'You had me worried for a moment,' confessed Celia Moreau as her daughter sat up and pushed a heavy wave of corn-coloured hair out of her eyes. 'There's time for you to bath and change before dinner, but only if you're quick about it,' she added warningly before she left the room.

Taking her advice, Lisa bathed quickly and rubbed herself vigorously with the towel afterwards, pausing only momentarily to finger the scar on her hip where they had had to cut into the flesh in order to reset the badly crushed bones. So many scars, she thought bitterly. So many reminders. Then, thrusting aside her thoughts, she reached for the talcum powder and sprinkled her body liberally before dressing, and joining her mother at the dinner table.

Lisa found it virtually impossible to sleep that night. Her aunt's suggestion that she should take on the job of looking after those two orphaned children kept thrusting its way into her mind and, despite her efforts, she could think of nothing else.

It was a ridiculous suggestion, she told herself. Living in the Karoo on a remote sheep farm did not appeal to her at all, and looking after two small children was a far cry from dealing successfully with intelligent twelve-year-olds. It was preposterous to imagine that she would be able to cope, and how would the children react to someone with a scarred face and an equally disfiguring limp? she wondered suddenly as bitterness welled up in her breast.

Rory's appalled features flashed through her mind, and she shrank inwardly from the whole idea as she switched on the bedside light and thrust aside the blankets to lower her feet on to the floor in search of her soft mules. A glass of warm cocoa might induce sleep, she decided as she pulled on her gown, but on her way to the door she paused in front of the full-length mirror and, almost against her will, she studied her reflection critically, and a trifle cynically.

She had always been small and slender, but she was now almost painfully thin, and her cheekbones stood out prominently in her pale face to throw deep shadows beneath wide-set blue eyes fringed heavily with pale gold lashes.

Her hair was the colour of ripe corn, and it waved naturally down on to her shoulders, but since the accident she deliberately combed it forward to hide the scar against her left temple, but there was no way she could hide the raised, sometimes livid scar along the side of her jaw. It stood out against her pale skin like a beacon, she thought, taunting her ruthlessly and making her believe everything Rory's cruel, horrified glance had implied.

Lisa's vision clouded at this point and, as always, the sensitive curves of her generous mouth went unnoticed, as did the tenderness and passion it implied. The small, straight nose and the firmly rounded chin suggested an inner strength, and the colour of her eyes changed to an arresting violet blue when she became excited. The minor lacerations on her face had healed to leave her delicately boned features undisturbed, but Lisa had progressed beyond the stage of finding anything pleasing in the face that stared back at her so steadily.

Her hand absently massaged her left hip and thigh as if in anticipation of the nagging pain which still gnawed at her after lengthy periods of remaining on her feet, and she sighed heavily as she turned from her reflected image and made her way along the darkened passage towards the kitchen.

Her mother's bedroom had been in darkness when she had passed it, but no sooner had she put the saucepan of milk on the stove when her mother walked into the kitchen, her slippered feet making no sound on the tiled floor.

'Could you do with some more company?' Celia Moreau asked quietly and, when Lisa nodded silently, she added more milk to that which was already in the saucepan and took upon herself the task of making them each a mug of cocoa.

Lisa hooked her cane over the back of the kitchen chair

and lowered herself into it, leaning her elbows on the table as she enviously watched her mother move about the kitchen. Her movements were fluid and without the jarring limp Lisa struggled so vainly to conquer.

'Your hip will take some time to heal,' the doctor had warned her. 'Don't expect miracles, but within less than a year you should be free of all discomfort and well on the way to walking normally.'

Lisa had listened calmly at the time, but her patience was severely tried at times when she found herself incapable of doing the simple little things which had once been second nature, and she hated having to cling to the rails for support whenever she climbed the two flights of steps up to their flat. She was only just beginning to drive her car again, and this, at least, afforded her a certain amount of pleasure and freedom, but she avoided meeting people as much as possible.

'You must try to forget the past, Lisa,' her mother remarked casually but shrewdly. 'It isn't good for you to brood over what happened, and you know it only leaves you restless and depressed.'

Lisa's fingers tightened on the mug of cocoa her mother had placed before her. 'I can't help remembering, and when I look in the mirror I sometimes wish I'd died as well.'

'*Lisa!*' Celia Moreau's face paled as she stared at her daugher in horror. 'Never say that again!'

'But my face——'

'Is scarred, yes,' her mother interrupted her forcefully. 'But the scars are mercifully not as disfiguring as you like to imagine, and you must be grateful for that.'

'Oh, Mother,' Lisa sighed unsteadily, a flicker of pain in the eyes she raised to her mother's. 'I've seen the way people stare at me, and——'

'Don't, my dear,' her mother silenced her hastily, and

Lisa began to despise herself for the film of tears in her mother's eyes. 'With time and care you'll be walking normally again, and the doctor promised that the scars would heal until they were barely noticeable.'

'And if they don't?' Lisa questioned in a frightened whisper.

'Then you could always consider the possibility of further surgery.'

Tears stung Lisa's eyelids and she blinked them away rapidly. 'I suppose you think I'm a fool.'

'No, my dear.' The hand that touched Lisa's arm was gentle and compassionate. 'You've had a very unfortunate experience, and you're very sensitive about it, that's all, but you'll get over it in time.'

Lisa shrugged tiredly. 'Yes, I suppose so.'

'Drink up, dear,' her mother suggested at length. 'It's time we went to bed.'

They said goodnight a few minutes later and went to their respective rooms, but it was some time before Lisa was able to shed her depression. The wind had subsided earlier in the evening, but not before it had brought the rain, and, as she lay listening to the patter of raindrops against her window, she wished she knew what the future had in store for her. The offer her aunt had made to her that afternoon was suddenly enticing, but a part of her still rejected the idea most forcibly. She tried to banish the subject from her mind, but found herself mentally compiling a list *for* and *against* the idea until she finally fell asleep from sheer exhaustion.

The sun was shining the next day for the first time in almost a week, and the sky was an incredible blue, Lisa noticed while she helped her mother pack away the Sunday lunch dishes, but a tense little silence, by no means the first that day, hovered between them as they moved about the small kitchen with its neat cupboards and red checkered curtains. Lisa knew the reason for the tense atmosphere, but could not bring herself to speak of it, and it was her mother who finally broached the subject when they sat down to their tea in the lounge.

'Lisa, have you thought any more about that job Molly offered you?'

'Yes, I have thought about it, but I can assure you I didn't do so intentionally,' Lisa admitted wryly.

'And?'

Lisa avoided her mother's direct blue gaze and shrugged her shoulders listlessly. 'I don't know.'

'If I were you, I'd jump at the chance.'

'Are you trying to get rid of me, Mother?' Lisa questioned, a hint of half-forgotten humour lurking in her voice.

'Of course not, my dear,' her mother replied indignantly, 'but I know how depressed you've become since the accident, and then there's Rory——'

'We won't discuss Rory, Mother, if you don't mind,' Lisa interrupted coldly with a glitter of ice in the depths of her eyes that had never been there before.

'I'm sorry,' Celia Moreau apologised contritely.

'No, *I'm* sorry,' Lisa contradicted a little ruefully, regretting her harshness with the one person who had stood by her so wonderfully during the past three months. 'You're right, though, Mother,' she added quietly. 'I've become depressed and irritable, and I can't seem to snap out of it.'

'You'll get over it in time, but not if you stay here where there's so much to remind you of the accident and everything that happened afterwards,' her mother told her wisely.

'I could be at the other end of the world, Mother, and I'd still be reminded of it,' Lisa stated a little impatiently.

'All I have to do is look in the mirror.'

'I told you, Lisa, you're unnecessarily touchy about those scars. They could have been much worse.'

'They were bad enough to make Rory——' Lisa bit her lip. Like her mother, she was trespassing on the very subject she had wanted to avoid.

'Forget about it, Lisa,' was her mother's whispered comment. 'If he had truly loved you, then your appearance would have made no difference to him, but as it is, he's not worth breaking your heart over.'

'Yes, I know that,' Lisa acknowledged readily, but deep down his rejection of her still hurt so much at times that it was almost impossible to bear. 'What would you do if I accepted this job Aunt Molly has offered me?'

'I would stay on here in the flat, of course. I have my work at the clothing store and I'm quite capable of looking after myself, you know.' Celia Moreau placed her empty tea-cup in the tray and eyed her daughter speculatively. 'Are you going to take the job?'

Lisa raised her hand almost without thinking and her fingers traced the scar on her face from ear to chin. 'I might.'

'It would be such a change from teaching.'

'Yes, it would.'

'The fresh, clean country air would be the best tonic anyone could possibly prescribe for you,' Celia Moreau continued persuasively.

'Mother ...'

'Don't hesitate, my dear,' her mother persisted, taking the telephone off the table beside the sofa and placing it on the padded armrest of Lisa's chair. 'Give Molly a ring and tell her you'll take the job before you change your mind again.'

'But I haven't decided finally,' Lisa protested desperately

as she shrank from the mere idea.

'Don't be silly, dear, of course you've decided.'

'Oh, Mother ...'

'Take this,' her mother smiled as she placed the receiver in Lisa's trembling hand. 'Now dial Molly's number.'

Lisa somehow found herself carrying out her mother's instructions, and she could never quite recall afterwards what she had said, but during the week that followed she became only too aware of having agreed to something which she still had severe doubts about. It was as if she had taken her fate into her own hands, and now there was no turning back.

Molly Anstey had contacted Erica Vandeleur on the telephone that same evening, and the wheels were set in motion. Erica Vandeleur had mentioned a tentative figure as salary which was sufficiently alluring, and it was finally decided that Lisa would drive herself up to Beaufort West on the Monday of the following week. Celia Moreau had not been too happy about this arrangement, but eventually agreed to it when Lisa promised faithfully that she would take the journey in easy stages.

The days seemed to fly past with an incredible swiftness, and it was on a misty Monday morning that Lisa found herself bidding her mother farewell and driving in an easterly direction towards Beaufort West. There was a lump in her throat when she left Cape Town behind her, but her interest in her surroundings quickened when she negotiated the bends in the road through the fruit and wine-producing valleys.

It was a new experience for her, travelling along this route, and when the sun dispersed with the mist clouds she stopped often to ease her aching hip, or to admire the spectacular scenery. At Paarl she glimpsed the KWV wine cellars, reputed to be the largest in the world, and then the scenic drive began along the Du Toitskloof Pass to Worcester and beyond. The mountains towered to the left and right of her as her small red Fiat finally gathered speed down into the picturesque Hex River Valley where the Barlinka vines were sprouting new young leaves and shoots in preparation for the coming season.

Lisa stopped at a vantage point to admire the vineyards and the homesteads built in the old Cape Dutch style. Her hand absently massaged her hip and thigh, but the breathtaking view made up in every way for the pain she was suffering at that moment. It was too soon, perhaps, to have attempted such a long journey, she realised, but she brushed aside the thought as she leaned against her car and eased her weight off her leg. She raised her hand to shade her eyes from the sun, and her glance dwelled on the beauty of the lush green valley spread out before her where spring had already invaded the vineyards. She had almost three hundred kilometres still to travel before she reached her destination, but she knew that the scenery would change almost drastically the moment she left the valley, so she lingered for almost half an hour before easing herself reluctantly into the car and driving further.

The Karoo was as hot and dusty as she had visualised it, with its sparse vegetation and scanty soil and, despite the discomfort of her aching hip, she drove through Matjiesfontein without stopping, glimpsing only briefly the Victorian houses with the original lamp-posts still lining the streets. Flags were flying from the masts of the elegantly restored hotel, but Lisa put her foot down on the accelerator and drove on to Lainsburg before stopping to fill up with petrol, and to snatch a light lunch at a café.

It was hot and dry in this semi-desert country, and she began to long for a cool, refreshing bath and a change of clothing. Her blouse was clinging to her back, and her cotton skirt no longer looked as fresh as it had when she left Cape Town after breakfast that morning. She had at least another two hours' travelling ahead of her, and the closer she came to her destination, the more apprehensive she became. Would the children accept her? Would she be able to cope?

A trickle of perspiration ran down her spine, and she shuddered as she climbed back into her car and resumed her journey into the heart of the sheep farming country. The sun beat down mercilessly on to the dry earth, and the road lay ahead of her, shimmering in the heat, and seemingly endless.

CHAPTER TWO

A PECULIAR whiteness had settled about Lisa's mouth when
Beaufort West loomed up ahead of her two hours later.
With its streets lined with pear trees and its green gardens
and playing fields, it seemed like an oasis in this desert-
like area, but pain marred her appreciation and, clenching
her teeth, she parked her car beneath a shady pear tree at
the side of the road.

Beads of perspiration stood out on her forehead as she
swallowed down a capsule for the pain with the remainder
of the water she had in her flask and, easing herself gingerly
out of the driver's seat, she leaned weakly against the car
for a few seconds before studying the directions she had
scribbled down so hastily. It all seemed perfectly simple,
she decided eventually and, dropping the small scrap of
paper into her handbag, she climbed back into her car and
drove a little further to the service station.

While the petrol pump attendant saw to the needs of her
car, Lisa sponged her face in the cloakroom and tried to
restore some order to her appearance. The capsule was
taking effect, and the pain was easing in her hip, but the
whiteness about her mouth, and the faint shadows beneath
her eyes lingered as a reminder. With the careful use of a
powder base she managed to conceal most of the damage,
but the tightness about her usually soft mouth remained
and, sighing tiredly, she snapped her bag shut and went out
into the hot afternoon sunshine.

From a public telephone at the local post office, Lisa
telephoned her mother to assure her of her safety and,

20

promising to write as soon as she could, she continued on
the last lap of her journey. Ten minutes later, however, she
was totally confused, and once again studying the directions her aunt had given her. She had taken the wrong
turning somehow, and had gone in a complete circle to find
herself back where she had started originally on the out-
skirts of the town.

'Where on earth did I go wrong?' she asked herself
loudly, but her voice was drowned by the sound of a small
truck crunching to an abrupt halt on the opposite side of
the road, and out of the cloud of dust a man appeared at her
side. He was a farmer, judging by the dusty grey pants and
khaki shirt he wore, and the weatherbeaten face was lowered in line with her car window.

'Having trouble?' he asked, pushing his shabby hat further back on to his grey head as he peered into her face
intently and searchingly.

Lisa was in the process of shrinking from him when she
realised that the scarred side of her face was turned away
from him.

'I'm afraid I'm a little lost,' she explained, deriding herself now for her sensitivity concerning her appearance.
'Could you direct me to the Vandeleur farm, please?'

'Vandeleur?' Grey eyes widened perceptibly. 'You mean
Adam Vandeleur?'

'That's his name, I believe,' Lisa remarked a little dryly,
holding the glance of the elderly man, who seemed to recover from his astonishment swiftly.

'You must be the young lady who's come to look after
Jacques Vandeleur's children.'

'That's right.'

'Well, I never!' the man exclaimed softly, lifting his hat
to scratch his grey head thoughtfully.

'The Vandeleur farm,' Lisa prodded gently, impatient

now to reach the end of her agonising journey. 'Could you direct me, please?'

'Oh, sure,' he said apologetically, thrusting his hat back on to his head to shade his eyes against the sun. 'Carry on with this road until it forks into two. Take the road to the left, and about twelve kilometres further you'll see the sign-post with Adam's name printed on it. It'll be on your left. Fairview is the name of the farm, and you can't miss it.'

'Thank you very much,' Lisa smiled up at him, starting the car and pushing the gear lever into position.

'It was a pleasure, miss.' He raised his hat politely. 'And good luck.'

Lisa frowned as she negotiated the uneven road, and a new uneasiness took possession of her as she recalled the man's parting words. *Good luck*. Would she be needing luck as an employee of Adam Vandeleur and his mother, or had the remark merely been a figure of speech?

At the fork in the road where she had originally taken the wrong turning, Lisa shrugged off her apprehensiveness, and twelve kilometres further, as the helpful farmer had informed her, she encountered the signpost indicating the turn-off to Fairview.

'This is it!' she told herself and, turning the nose of her dusty Fiat towards the direction indicated, she drove as carefully as possible along the bumpy farm track towards the house which was barely visible beyond the row of poplar and gum trees.

The two-storied homestead with its trellised verandah was far removed from the primitive farmhouse Lisa had expected, and the woman who came out of the house to welcome her was not at all as Lisa had visualised Erica Vandeleur. Tall and frail-looking, she was a woman whose age Lisa judged to be well into the sixties, but there was a certain elegance about her which Lisa had not expected from a woman who had lived nearly all her life on a farm.

Erica Vandeleur came swiftly down the steps as Lisa stepped carefully out of the car, and she winced inwardly when she transferred her weight on to her left foot and felt that familiar sharp pain shoot from her hip into her thigh. Grey-green eyes swept Lisa from head to foot, taking in the greyness of her pallor and the way her knuckles whitened on the carved handle of her walking-stick, then the older woman banished Lisa's initial nervousness by taking complete charge of the situation.

'Good heavens, child, you must be exhausted. Daisy!' She clapped her hands and a woman appeared as if she had been waiting explicitly for that call. 'Take Miss Moreau's suitcases up to her room, and tell Petrus to park her car in one of the vacant garages.' She turned then and gripped Lisa's free arm, giving her added support as if it was the most natural thing on earth. 'Come in out of this heat, and ... Oh, dear! I'm afraid in all the excitement I forgot to introduce myself.' A warm, friendly smile flashed across the thin, wrinkled face. 'I'm Erica Vandeleur.'

Without waiting for her introduction to be acknowledged, she ushered Lisa into the large, cool entrance hall with its gleaming yellow-wood floors, stinkwood chests, and mirrored hat-stand.

'I suppose you'd welcome a wash and a change while I order a fresh pot of tea?'

'That would be lovely, thank you,' Lisa admitted a little breathlessly, glancing ruefully at her dusty crumpled appearance.

'Daisy, show Miss Moreau up to her room,' Erica Vandeleur instructed the woman when she entered the house with Lisa's luggage, then she glanced almost apologetically at Lisa. 'I've put you in a room upstairs. I hope the stairs won't be too inconvenient for you?'

'I'll manage perfectly, thank you,' Lisa assured her a little stiffly, not quite sure whether she approved of the woman's pointed reference to her disability, but Erica Vandeleur was already making her way across the hall to the back of the house.

'Come down to the living-room as soon as you're ready, my dear,' she said over her shoulder.

Lisa nodded and followed Daisy upstairs, making use of the carved, old-fashioned balustrade and her walking-stick for the necessary support, and thankful that Erica Vandeleur had not remained in the hall to witness her ungainly ascension to the upper floor.

The bedroom which had been prepared for Lisa was large and sunny. She had her own private bathroom which was tiled and reasonably modern, and the fringed bedside lamps on either side of the big double bed with its brass canopy made her realise that the Vandeleurs obviously generated their own electricity.

'Shall I unpack for the madam?' Daisy offered politely, her watchful brown eyes observing Lisa sympathetically as she limped towards the window.

Lisa, unaware of the sympathy she had evoked, turned from her hasty surveillance of the well-kept garden with its circular driveway, and smiled at the woman hovering respectfully at the foot of the bed where she had deposited Lisa's suitcases.

'That won't be necessary, thank you.'

Daisy nodded and flashed a smile at Lisa. 'Any time the madam may need anything, the madam may just call me.'

Lisa thanked her, impatient now to have a few moments alone in the room she was to occupy for the next few months, and, as the door closed behind Daisy, she glanced about her appreciatively, taking in the Kiaat dressing-table with the matching wardrobe, the small writing desk with an upright wooden chair pushed neatly underneath it, and the large padded armchair in the corner beside the bed. An olive-green carpet covered the entire floor space, and the lemon-coloured curtains matched the quilted bed-spread. It was a pleasing room, Lisa decided as she lifted one of her suitcases on to the bed and searched for a clean blouse and skirt. If Mrs Vandeleur was expecting her downstairs for tea, then there would not be time for more than a quick wash and a change of clothing, she realised ruefully. The bath she longed for would just have to wait.

When she ventured downstairs some minutes later, she felt reasonably refreshed and, after glancing about her a little uncertainly, she walked slowly towards the door that stood invitingly open across the hall. Erica Vandeleur was seated on a stinkwood bench with padded cushions of wine-red velvet, and on the low table in front of her a tray of tea stood waiting. She indicated that Lisa should sit down beside her, and poured the tea at once.

'You must be extremely tired after your long journey,' she remarked, offering Lisa the plate of small, flaky jam tarts.

'I'm a little stiff, yes,' Lisa admitted, yielding to the temptation and helping herself to one of the tarts. 'I stopped several times along the way, and also for tea and lunch, which gave me a few minutes to stretch my legs before going on.'

'Tell me, how is dear Molly?' Mrs Vandeleur questioned in her warm, cultured voice.

'Still trying to manipulate the lives of others in the nicest, kindest way,' Lisa smiled faintly. 'She sends her love.'

'I can remember so well when she was still at university with my niece Peggy,' Mrs Vandeleur began reminiscently. 'Molly and Peggy spent a number of their holidays on the

farm with us, and Molly was such a vivacious creature, I remember. After graduating she married Luke Anstey who
was chief pilot for a chartered airline company in the Cape,
and he died so tragically a few years later.' Erica Vandeleur's grey-green eyes clouded, possibly with the memory
of her own, and very recent grief. 'I'm surprised Molly
never married again.'

'Aunt Molly maintains that those five years of marriage
were the most idyllic any woman could have wished for,
and no one else could ever take the place of the man who'd
made them so.'

'It's such a pity.' Erica Vandeleur seemed to be speak-
ing to herself. 'Death is always so dreadfully final, and for
those who remain behind life never seems to be the same
again.'

'I'm sorry,' Lisa murmured inadequately, her own
thoughts returning to that dreadful morning when her
friend Sandy had been laughing and talking excitedly about
the coming holidays, only to have the life crushed out of
her a few minutes later.

The perspiration stood out on Lisa's forehead at the
memory of it, and she shook herself free of her thoughts
with a visible effort. 'Where are the children?' she asked.

'Josh and Kate?' The older woman came out of her
reverie and gestured vaguely. 'Oh, good heavens, they must
be somewhere about the place. I'm afraid they've become
a little wild over the past months. I find it impossible trying to keep up with them, and Adam—that's my son—has
never had much patience with children. At thirty-eight he's
still a bachelor, and bachelors don't always take kindly to
having their well-ordered existence disrupted by two
rowdy, energetic children, but, in his own way, I have no
doubt that he is fond of them.'

They finished their tea in silence and Lisa had the opportunity to look about her. The furnishings were old, but solid, and the cream-coloured carpet added a touch of brightness to the living-room with its wine-red curtains and upholstered chairs. Landscape paintings adorned the walls, and above the stone fireplace hung two lethal-looking sabres, their handles intricately carved, and their curved blades crossed and pointing towards the ceiling.

'My late husband travelled extensively before our marriage,' Mrs Vandeleur explained when she followed the direction of Lisa's interested glance. 'Those swords were brought from India many years ago.'

Lisa met the older woman's direct scrutiny, and stiffened, her fingers going self-consciously and protectively towards the scar on the side of her jaw, but there was no sign of revulsion in those grey-green eyes.

'I know about your unfortunate accident,' Erica Vandeleur explained with a warmth and gentleness that touched Lisa deeply and set her at her ease. 'I haven't told anyone, not even Adam, and the subject shan't be mentioned unless you wish to do so. We need your help, Lisa,' she added, using Lisa's name with natural ease, 'and I would like to think we can help to restore you in some way to your former self.'

Lisa's eyes filled with tears and she looked away hastily. 'You're very kind, Mrs Vandeleur.'

The sound of raised children's voices shattered the ensuing silence, and two dishevelled, muddy little figures stampeded their way into the living-room, only to come to an abrupt halt when they noticed Lisa.

Erica Vandeleur stifled an exclamation of horror. 'Don't come any closer!' she warned quickly. 'You'll leave footprints on the carpet! I suggest you both go upstairs and clean yourselves up a bit before you come down again so I can introduce you properly to Miss Moreau.'

'Oh, Gran, why can't you in—in—why can't we meet her now?' grumbled one of the dirty-faced imps.

'Because you're so dirty at the moment it's difficult to see who's who,' their grandmother stated firmly. 'Go upstairs at once and do as I say.'

The two children obeyed reluctantly, but they could be heard complaining bitterly as they made their way up to their room, and Lisa stifled a smile as the older woman glanced at her exasperatedly.

'I don't envy you your task,' she stated blandly. 'If you're ever in need of assistance, you could always call in Adam's help. They have a healthy respect for him, if nothing else.'

The children returned to the living-room some minutes later with their faces and hands scrubbed reasonably clean, and although their clothes still displayed the ravages of their muddy game, they had taken the trouble to exchange their dirty boots for clean sandals.

Dark-haired and dark-eyed, the twins waited just inside the living-room door for their grandmother's nod of approval before they ventured further into the room, and Lisa knew herself to be stared at with avid interest.

'Lisa, I would like you to meet my grandchildren,' Erica Vandeleur smiled. 'Josh and Kate, this is Miss Moreau, the young lady I told you about.'

Tanned and sturdily built, they faced Lisa, and she felt herself grow tense as their eyes searched the hollows and planes of her face with its livid scar. She waited for what she had feared most, but their childish little faces never registered anything other than curiosity, and her relief was suddenly so great that she felt choked and shaky.

'Are you going to look after us?' Josh demanded while his sister looked on shyly.

'If you'll let me, yes.'

'Can you play marbles?'

It was a question of some importance, Lisa realised, and meeting the little boy's unfaltering gaze she replied, 'Yes, I think so.'

'That's all right, then,' he said, and the matter was obviously settled as far as Josh was concerned. Ignoring Lisa now, he turned to his grandmother. 'Can we go and play again?'

'If you play in your room, yes,' their grandmother replied firmly. 'It's nearly time for your bath, and then it's supper and bed for you two.'

'Oh, Gran!' they chorussed disappointedly, but Erica Vandeleur remained adamant.

'No arguments, please. You both know the rules laid down by your Uncle Adam.'

'But Uncle Adam won't be home until late this evening,' Josh protested loudly.

'That makes no difference.'

Josh scowled darkly. 'Oh, dash it!'

'Joshua!'

'Sorry, Gran,' he muttered hastily, tugging at the skirt of his sister's dress. 'Come along, Kate.'

'If you would like to go up to your room to settle yourself in, then please feel free,' Mrs Vandeleur suggested the moment they were alone. 'The children are in the room next to yours, and I'd be grateful if you'd see to it that they bath at five o'clock and put on their pyjamas before coming down to the kitchen for their supper. They have all their other meals with us in the dining-room, but Adam seldom wants to eat before seven in the evenings, and by that time the children are restless and tired.' She paused for a moment before adding: 'You will, of course, have all your meals with us in the dining-room.'

'I wouldn't mind eating with the children in the evenings,' Lisa said hastily, but Erica Vandeleur would not hear of it.

'Adam will naturally want to speak to you personally, but as he isn't here this evening he'll most probably see you first thing tomorrow morning.'

'Thank you,' Lisa murmured, rising to her feet.

'And Lisa,' the older woman smiled up at her, 'dinner in the evenings is informal. Adam prefers it that way.'

Upstairs in her room a few minutes later, Lisa unpacked her suitcases and tried to quell the nervousness that was welling up inside her. For some inexplicable reason the thought of meeting Adam Vandeleur disturbed her. Despite the warm welcome Erica Vandeleur had given her, it was Adam who would be her employer, and she somehow had the feeling that he was not going to be so easy to please.

Josh and Kate shared a room similar to her own, Lisa discovered later, except that it was furnished entirely in white, with a blue carpet on the floor, and blue floral curtains at the window. A section of the large room had been partitioned off as a play area, and neither of the children looked too happy when Lisa interrupted their pillow fight to announce that it was time for their bath.

Kate was the first to relent and, in the adjoining bathroom, she allowed Lisa to help her bath. When Lisa eventually wrapped a towel around her pink, glowing little body, she discovered that Josh was an entirely different proposition when it came to having her assist him in any way.

He stripped off his clothes and climbed into the bath, but when Lisa approached him, he announced with a certain haughtiness: 'I can bath myself.'

'Of course,' Lisa replied tactfully, turning towards the door, but as her hand touched the handle, he demurred.

'You can wash my back, if you like,' he suggested, and Lisa hastily hid her smile of amusement as she sat down on the edge of the bath and soaped his back thoroughly.

This was Josh's way of indicating that he accepted her, and Lisa acknowledged this with the solemnity it deserved.

Later, as she searched for their clean pyjamas and helped them dress, Josh questioned her in that direct manner of his.

'Have you always walked like that?' he demanded as she limped towards him and handed him his pyjama jacket.

She met his candid dark gaze, and, finding nothing there but the casual interest of a child, her nervousness and reluctance to discuss herself evaporated.

'No ... not always,' she admitted, seating herself on the bed and assisting him with the buttons.

'Did you have an accident?' Josh persisted.

'Yes.'

There was a strained little silence as if both children were recalling the accident which had robbed them of both their parents, then Kate sat down beside Lisa and shyly touched her cheek, her small fingers exploring the long scar. Lisa felt herself grow tense as she stared down at the child, but she did not repulse her.

'You're very pretty,' Kate said eventually, and the unexpected compliment from a child she hardly knew seemed to wash away some of the coldness and bitterness of the past months.

'Thank you, Kate,' Lisa said unsteadily, hugging the child impulsively.

'Did it hurt much?' Josh wanted to know, gesturing towards the scar.

'Yes. Physically as well as mentally,' she could have replied, but Josh would not have understood, so she said instead: 'It did hurt quite a bit, yes.'

'Are you a teacher?' Josh changed the subject as if her appearance no longer concerned him.

'Yes, I am.'

'We're going to school next term,' Kate stated importantly.

'So I believe,' Lisa smiled at her.

'Are teachers very cross always?' Kate questioned her with a flicker of anxiety in her eyes.

'Not always.'

'Are you?'

'Only when the children give me reason to be,' Lisa smiled, picking up the brush and brushing Kate's dark hair until it curled softly into her neck.

'Uncle Adam's always cross, and he isn't even a teacher,' Josh announced with a scowl, and Lisa suddenly recalled Erica Vandeleur's statement that the children had a healthy respect for their uncle, if nothing else.

If nothing else. Surely the fact that Josh and Kate were his late brother's children would have forged a bond between them? Certainly it was a good thing for the children to respect their uncle and guardian, but that was not enough. Children needed to love and *be* loved, but Josh's remark made Lisa wonder whether they were receiving the love and care they needed from the man who had taken the place of their father.

'Perhaps it's just that your uncle is busy and has other things on his mind,' Lisa found herself making excuses for a man she had never met, and who was beginning to assume a formidable and frightening shape.

'Do you think so?' Josh wanted to know with disbelief and eager acceptance fighting for supremacy on his small features.

'I'm only guessing,' Lisa prevaricated hastily. 'I haven't met your uncle yet.'

'You'll meet him tomorrow,' Josh said dully, the light of hope dying in his eyes.

'Yes,' Lisa murmured with a feeling of trepidation. 'To-morrow.'

In the spacious and modernised kitchen, under the curious surveillance of the servants, Lisa saw to it that the children ate their supper and drank their milk before she took them up to their room and tucked them in for the night.

On the small cupboard between their beds stood a framed photograph of a man and a woman, and Lisa knew at once that it was a photograph of the children's parents. Josh and Kate had inherited their colouring from both their mother and their father, Lisa realised, but it was Jacques Vandeleur's face that interested her the most. It was a friendly, laughing face, ruggedly handsome and youthful. If the children's uncle was anything like his younger brother, then she had nothing to fear, she thought, but she was perhaps hoping for too much.

Suppressing a sigh, she switched off the light and left the children's room. With more than a half hour to spare before she was to join Erica Vandeleur in the dining-room for dinner, Lisa soaked her weary body in a hot, scented bath and hauled out a blue silk dress which was cool and not too decorative. After hurriedly applying her make-up and brushing her hair to a golden sheen, she went downstairs, but, as there was no sign as yet of Mrs Vandeleur, she went out on to the long verandah.

She had heard of the spectacular sunsets in the Karoo, but the sight that met her eyes surpassed her wildest imagination, and she could not prevent the exclamation of delight that passed her lips. The sun, a red ball of fire in the west, cast a golden hue over the earth, bringing this partially barren country to life in a breathtaking way, and transforming it into a mysterious and magical paradise.

The dry, dusty earth now looked fertile and rich, and a

silence descended on the veld which was disturbed only by the occasional bleating of the sheep. There was an undeniable aura of peace and tranquillity in the air, and as she clutched at the wooden rail and drew the fresh, spicy air deep into her lungs, she felt the tensions of the day falling away from her. She was suddenly incredibly glad that she had allowed herself to be persuaded into coming to this seemingly desolate part of the country.

CHAPTER THREE

LISA awoke the following morning to the distinct sound of a dog barking beneath her window, and for a moment she stared about her confusedly before she realised where she was. It was an unusual experience for her to be awakened by the barking of a dog and the bleating of sheep instead of the roar of the city traffic, and she lay for a moment, acquainting herself with her surroundings, until the thought of her impending meeting with Adam Vandeleur sent her scrambling out of bed.

She opened her window wide to let in the freshness of the tangy early morning air, pausing for a moment to admire the dew-drenched garden sparkling in the slanting rays of the rising sun, but there was no time to linger in front of the window as she would have liked to do, and she hurried through to the bathroom.

Lisa dressed herself with added care that morning, and took even greater care with her make-up in an effort to camouflage slightly the livid scar on her face. Her neat cream skirt was of a non-crushable material, and her crisp white blouse had withstood the journey well in the over-full suitcase. Her hair had a healthy sheen to it after a vigorous brushing, and it waved softly on to her shoulders. There was still a faintly bruised look beneath her eyes, but she had suffered no ill-effects after the tiring journey the day before, and felt surprisingly refreshed.

Josh and Kate were dressed and ready to accompany her downstairs when she looked in on them a few minutes later and, as they made their way down to the dining-room, Lisa

steeled herself for her meeting with their uncle, but Erica
Vandeleur was alone in the dining-room.

'Adam went out early this morning,' she explained, quick
to sum up Lisa's nervous glance about the room with its
long oak table and tall dresser. 'He'll see you as soon as he
returns.'

A feeling of momentary relief swept through Lisa, but
she knew that the inevitable was only being postponed as
she helped herself to a slice of home-made bread and
poured herself a cup of aromatically brewed coffee.

The children behaved exceptionally well at the table,
and, judging by the way they consumed their porridge and
eggs, they both possessed healthy appetites. Erica Vandeleur, despite her firmness, obviously adored her grandchildren. It was there in the way she looked at them, and
laughed with them over some amusing incident, and Lisa
observed the eagerness to please in the two little faces that
were so alike except for a subtle difference in the shape of
their mouths and eyes.

After breakfast Lisa took the children up to their room
and kept them occupied with plasticine while she drew up
some sort of daily roster, but she had not progressed very
far when Daisy knocked on the door and entered the room.

'Master Adam would like to see the madam in his study,'
she announced, and the look that passed between the twins
did not exactly dispel Lisa's anxiety.

Instructing the children to continue with what they
were doing, Lisa followed Daisy from the room and down
the stairs into the hall. Daisy's buxom figure led the way
down a short passage leading off the hall, and into a room
with books lining the shelves against the walls, and silver
trophies carelessly displayed above the fireplace. The room
was empty, however, and Lisa glanced questioningly at
Daisy.

Lisa nodded and swallowed down her nervousness when she finally found herself alone.

She stared down at the wide oak desk and felt like a young first year student who had been called to the Dean's office, instead of an adult woman of twenty-four with more than two years of teaching behind her. It was ridiculous to feel so nervous, she told herself, but her eyes darted apprehensively from the pile of farming magazines on the corner of the desk to the pipe and tobacco pouch lying on the green blotter. They told her nothing, except that her employer was an avid reader and a pipe smoker and, raising her glance to the books in the shelves, she sought her answer there, but the sound of a step in the passage made her turn swiftly towards the door.

A bulk of a man filled the doorway, and Lisa's startled glance was captured by dark, penetrating eyes that had a shattering effect on her nervous system. There was a wild fluttering in her throat like a caged bird seeking frantically for escape, and her breathing felt oddly restricted as she stared back helplessly for what seemed like interminable seconds before his eyes released her and allowed her to breathe easier. Massive-shouldered and slim-hipped, Adam Vandeleur was well over two metres tall, but, despite his enormous physique, his movements were lithe, she noticed as he walked round to the other side of his desk.

'I apologise for keeping you waiting, Miss Moreau,' he said in a voice that was deep, like the rumble of distant thunder. 'Please sit down.'

Lisa obeyed, hooking her walking-stick unobtrusively over the arm of her chair, and realising for the first time that her leg was shaking. She waited in diffident silence while he seated himself in the padded swivel chair behind his desk and picked up a cigarette case.

'Do you mind if I smoke?' he asked, and Lisa shook her

head, taking the opportunity to observe him more closely while he took a cigarette and lit it.

His short, crisp black hair was greying at the temples, and the sun had tanned his skin to a deep ochre. Unlike his brother Jacques, Adam was rugged and not at all handsome, Lisa decided as her nervous glance slid over the broad forehead, the high-bridged nose that showed signs of having been broken at some stage, and the square, resolute jaw with the slight cleft in the chin. There was strength of character in the harsh lines of his face, but her pulses behaved erratically when her glance lingered briefly on the hard mouth with the hint of sensuality in the wide lower lip.

Adam Vandeleur, ruthless and tough, was a man of the veld, she concluded her observations, lowering her glance guiltily when she realised that she had been caught staring.

'You're a teacher, I believe,' he remarked, his dark eyes narrowed as he observed her through a screen of smoke.

'I am a teacher, yes.'

'What made you resign your post to take on a job of this nature?' he questioned, his eyes intent upon her face and unnerving her so completely that she stammered foolishly.

'I d-didn't actually resign. I—I obtained leave of absence for a few months.'

'Why?' he rapped out the word like a command.

'I—I was involved in an accident.'

Lisa felt, more than saw, his eyes sliding over the prominent scar along the side of her jaw, and she stiffened automatically, but after that brief, cursory glance his expressionless eyes met hers again.

'Was it a car accident?'

'Yes.'

'You've obviously recovered sufficiently from this ... accident,' he continued, the slight pause in his voice placing her instantly on her guard. 'I fail to see why you couldn't return to the work you were trained for.'

'There—there were other reasons,' Lisa stammered, raising her chin in a faint gesture of defiance, but when he continued to stare at her as if expecting a detailed explanation, she added abruptly: 'Personal reasons.'

Adam Vandeleur's black eyebrows rose fractionally as if her reluctance to explain annoyed him, then he stubbed out his cigarette and rose to his feet, thrusting his thumbs into the broad leather belt that hugged his slim hips as he walked round the desk towards her.

'I gather my mother gave you some idea of what's expected of you, but there are a few things I would like to add,' he said harshly as he walked across to the window and stared out into the garden, giving Lisa an excellent view of his broad, formidable back and the long muscular legs clad in tight-fitting khaki pants. 'Keep the children out of the grazing camps, and don't allow them to mess around with the farm machinery. The shearing shed and the stables are forbidden to them, and most of all ...' He paused, turning to face her, and his dark brown eyes pinned her ruthlessly to her chair. 'Keep them out from under my feet. Is that understood?'

'Yes, Mr Vandeleur,' Lisa managed nervously.

'Now, about your salary.' He mentioned a sum that almost doubled the figure his mother had quoted and, misinterpreting her gasp of surprise, he asked stonily, 'Is the amount not sufficient?'

'No, no! It's far more than I'd expected,' she hastened to correct him, shrinking inwardly beneath those rapier sharp eyes that missed absolutely nothing.

'I'm quite prepared to pay that amount, and more, to restore some of the original order to my home, Miss Moreau,' that deep voice rumbled on harshly, and a mocking expression flashed across his rugged face as he observed her raised eyebrows. 'Does that shock you?'

'They're your late brother's children.'

'Exactly,' he snapped, coming towards her and forcing her to crane her neck to look up at him. 'Fate has thrust them into my care, and I shall just have to make the best of the situation.'

'You care about their happiness, don't you?' she questioned him daringly, but her hands clenched the arms of her chair so tightly that her fingers ached.

'Naturally,' he smiled briefly, but the smile never reached those hard eyes. 'They'll get whatever they might need, just as long as they don't interfere in the orderly existence I've created for myself.'

'I see,' Lisa said weakly, and a deep-seated fury uncurled itself within her at the selfishness and callousness of this man. There was not an ounce of sympathy and compassion in Adam Vandeleur's powerful body for the two young children who had been placed in his care, and she understood suddenly the wistful expression on Josh and Kate's faces when they spoke of their uncle and guardian.

'I don't think we have anything further to discuss,' Adam Vandeleur dismissed her curtly, and Lisa rose from her chair, in a hurry now to escape from this disturbing man.

'Just a moment!' His voice, like a clap of thunder, stopped her as her hand touched the brass doorhandle, and her nerves seemed to jar uncomfortably as she turned to face him, realising at once the reason for her detention when she saw his eyes on the walking-stick she leaned on. 'Have you injured your ankle?'

Lisa went cold beneath his scrutiny. 'No, it's—it's a hip injury I got in the accident.'

Those dark eyes raked her mercilessly now from head to foot. 'This alters the position entirely.'

'You—you mean as far as the job is concerned?'

'I do mean that, yes.'

Lisa could not remember ever being stirred to such anger, and her eyes glittered coldly as they met his. 'Because I have a slight physical disability it doesn't mean that I'm mentally deficient, Mr Vandeleur.'

His mouth tightened perceptibly. 'I'm not questioning your mental capabilities, Miss Moreau, but I doubt whether you're physically capable of handling the twins. They are very lively for their age.'

'I'll manage,' she said abruptly.

'I very much doubt it.'

'You could at least give me the opportunity to prove myself,' Lisa said accusingly, and the bitterness and disillusionment of the past months was clearly visible in the deep blue eyes that met his so steadily, and in the tightness about her normally soft mouth.

'I intend to give you that opportunity,' Adam Vandeleur said at length, his biceps bulging and straining against the short sleeves of his shirt as he moved the chair she had vacated out of his way and walked towards her. 'You have a month, Miss Moreau,' he warned, towering above her smallness so menacingly that she shrank against the door. 'If, at the end of that month, you find the physical strain too much, or if I'm not satisfied with the way you've managed the twins, I shall have no compunction in replacing you.'

'Thank you,' Lisa murmured, a tremor of fear rippling through her slight body.

'Don't thank me, Miss Moreau,' he mocked her. 'After a month you may wish you hadn't been so eager to prove yourself.' He nodded abruptly. 'You may go.'

Tears of bitterness and anger filled her eyes and, groping blindly for the brass door handle, she turned it and walked as quickly as she could from the study. Adam Vandeleur was the most objectionable man she had ever met! He had shattered her sadly floundering confidence with a callousness that had bordered on cruelty, but, as she paused for breath on the landing between the two floors, a new and almost frightening anger came to her rescue.

She would show Adam Vandeleur! She would show him, even if it killed her, that she was capable of looking after the twins as well as anyone else could.

She managed to regain her composure before entering the children's room, and two pairs of brown eyes were raised at once to stare at her with intense curiosity. A dog barked excitely in the garden below their window, and Lisa looked out just in time to see Adam Vandeleur disappearing round the corner of the house with a magnificent-looking Alsatian at his side, and she shivered involuntarily at the thought of having to confront this man every day for the next four months.

Josh could no longer contain his curiosity and, as Lisa turned away from the window, he asked: 'Did you see Uncle Adam?'

'Yes, I did,' Lisa replied evenly, seating herself on a small wooden chair to ease the weight off her leg.

Forgetting entirely about the mechanical crane he had been so absorbed in, Josh demanded: 'What did Uncle Adam say?'

'He said plenty,' Lisa thought bitterly, but as she stared into the two anxious faces staring up at her, she smiled. 'He said I must see to it that the two of you don't get up to mischief.'

'What's mischief?' Kate wanted to know.

'Well, it means that you shouldn't do anything you're not supposed to do,' Lisa explained patiently.

Josh frowned and looked vaguely suspicious. 'What aren't we supposed to do?'

'You're not to go anywhere near the grazing camps, the stables, or the shearing shed,' she ticked their uncle's instructions off on her fingers. 'And you're to stay away from the farm machinery.'

'We know that,' Josh scowled, picking up his temporarily forgotten crane.

'But I didn't,' Lisa explained, 'and as this is the first time I've ever been on a farm, I suppose your uncle thought it best that he should make me aware of these things.'

Kate stared at Lisa over the droopy head of the rag doll she clutched against her. 'Have you never been on a farm before?'

Lisa shook her head. 'No, never.'

'Where do you stay?'

'I've lived in Cape Town all my life.'

Josh looked up from his manipulations of the toy crane and stared at Lisa thoughtfully. 'We went to Cape Town once with our mummy and daddy, and we went up the mountain in a—in a——'

'Cable car,' Lisa supplemented helpfully.

'Yes,' he nodded, his eyes lighting up with excitement as he recalled the memory. 'Gosh, it was exciting, but Kate cried 'cause she was scared.'

'I *didn't* cry, and I *wasn't* scared,' Kate protested, a mutinous expression on her small, rounded face.

'You *were* scared,' Josh insisted.

'I *wasn't*!'

'Stop it, both of you!' Lisa ordered sharply as Kate hurled herself at her brother, but neither of them heard her and, gripping their flailing arms in mid-air, she was forced to drag them apart. They stood breathing heavily and glaring at each other for a few moments, but then their anger subsided as quickly as it had flared, and they lowered their eyes guiltily beneath Lisa's reproving glance.

'There's nothing wrong with being a little scared of the things you don't know,' Lisa said quietly, placing an arm about each of them. 'I was scared too the first time I went up the mountain in the cable car.'

'Were you really?' Josh questioned disbelievingly.

'Yes, I was,' Lisa confessed. 'Not everyone is as brave as you are, Josh.'

His chest seemed to swell with pride. 'Is it good to be brave?'

'Very good,' Lisa replied, but as she felt Kate wriggling uncomfortably in the circle of her arm, she added hastily, 'But it's also good to be a little scared at times. If you're scared, then you'll be careful, and in that way you won't do anything that is harmful, or dangerous.'

Kate's wriggling stilled instantly, and out of the corner of her eye Lisa glimpsed a satisfied expression on the little girl's face.

'Do you think our mummy and daddy crashed their plane because they weren't careful?'

'Oh, no,' Lisa hastened to assure Josh. 'I think they must have been very careful, but accidents do happen, and ...' she paused, the sound of crunching metal and shattering glass invading her mind as she heard herself add unsteadily, 'We don't always understand why things happen, but we must learn to accept them as the will of God.'

A lengthy silence prevailed; a silence filled with the haunting memory of a girl's happy, carefree laughter moments before death swooped down to claim her, and then, as the agony of what had followed seared through her, Lisa became aware of Josh and Kate observing her strangely.

'You look sad, and you're crying,' Kate observed curiously, and Lisa's hands flew to her cheeks to find them hot and damp.

'I'm being silly,' she laughed a little shakily, brushing away the evidence of her tears with her fingertips and pulling herself together.

'We don't cry any more 'cause Gran told us our mummy and daddy are in heaven with the angels, and one day we'll see them again.'

'That's very true,' Lisa replied to Josh's remark with a matching sincerity and, thrusting aside her unhappy thoughts, she smiled at them and took their hands in hers. 'Come on, let's go outside so you can show me the garden.'

The twins were delighted at the prospect of acting as her guide, but, for children so young, they were surprisingly thoughtful about dampening their enthusiasm and exuberance, and keeping in mind the fact that Lisa might have difficulty in keeping pace with them as they introduced her to all their secret places in the garden with its smooth lawns and vast assortment of shrubs.

It seemed impossible to Lisa that such a lush green paradise could exist in the heart of this dry, acrid semi-desert, but, as she gently fingered the heavily veined petals of a pink camellia, she silently mocked her own ignorance.

This was a world she had not known before; a world far removed from the city with its hustle and bustle, its petrol fumes, and lifeless concrete buildings. Her ears, acquainted only with the ceaseless roar of traffic, delighted now in the sounds of nature all about her, and she relaxed, a smile of tranquillity softening the rigid contours of her face and bringing a half-forgotten sparkle to eyes where shadows had lurked moments before.

The twins laughed excitedly as they went in pursuit of a butterfly, and the smile lingered on Lisa's lips as she walked slowly across the lawn to join them. They *were* lively for their age, as Adam Vandeleur had pointed out, and they involved Lisa in their games until that familiar sharp pain in her hip forced her to cease her participation. Josh and Kate's disappointment was evident, but they overcame it quickly and continued with their boisterous game while Lisa sat on a wooden bench beneath a shady tree to keep a watchful eye on them.

Erica Vandeleur served tea on the verandah that morning, and the children helped themselves to several freshly-baked scones before they wandered off again to play in the garden. Lisa stood up hastily to follow them, but Erica Vandeleur gestured her back into her chair.

'They won't go too far—not while there are still scones left on the plate,' she smiled reassuringly, and Lisa relaxed only to find those grey-green eyes observing her questioningly. 'Did Adam see you earlier this morning?'

Lisa shifted uncomfortably in her chair as she recalled her interview with this woman's son. 'Mr Vandeleur did speak to me this morning, yes.'

'He's been so busy since my son Jacques died that he seldom has time to relax. It's nothing unusual these days to see him for the first time at dinner in the evenings.' Erica Vandeleur sighed and shook her grey head sadly. 'Heaven knows, this farm is big enough for two men, but with the added responsibility of Jacques' farm it's become a near impossible task.'

'Wouldn't the best solution be to employ a manager for the other farm?' Lisa questioned a little hesitantly.

'Suitable managers aren't that easy to find these days,' the older woman explained, 'but Adam has mentioned the possibility of employing someone at the end of this month, and I can't tell you what a relief it would be to me.'

'Do the two farms join each other?'

'Unfortunately not,' Erica Vandeleur shook her head. 'The Jacksons' farm lies between Fairview and Waverley. Mr Jackson and his daughter, Willa, have helped Adam a

great deal, but things can't continue like this indefinitely.
Adam is a strong healthy man, but there's a limit to everyone's endurance and, with Willa assisting him so admirably,
I'm afraid ...' She paused, a frown settling between her
brows, then, as Lisa stared at her curiously, she uttered a
disparaging sound. 'It doesn't matter. I'm just being foolish,
I suppose.'

A peculiar little silence settled between them; a silence
during which Lisa wondered what exactly Erica Vandeleur
was afraid of. Was she perhaps afraid that, with Willa Jackson assisting him with the work on Waverley, he might
eventually consider marrying the girl? Surely a girl with
the experience and knowledge of farming would make an
admirable wife for a man like Adam Vandeleur? Or was it
something else that Erica Vandeleur feared; something
which Lisa was not aware of perhaps?

The silence was broken when Josh and Kate bounded up
the steps on to the verandah to help themselves to the remainder of the scones and, dismissing her thoughts with a
careless shrug, Lisa excused herself and accepted the
children's offer to show her more of the farm.

The sun was warm against her pale skin as she followed
Josh and Kate through the garden and, not for the first
time since her arrival on Fairview, she drew the air deep
into her lungs and marvelled at the clean freshness of it.
It must be marvellous, she thought, to live in this environ-
ment every day of one's life, to breathe in the tangy air of
the veld, and to live so close to nature that you eventually
become an inseparable part of it. She recalled her disparaging remarks concerning the Karoo when her aunt had
first suggested her coming here, and, although her opinion
had not altered entirely, there was something about this
desolate land that appealed to her, making her feel ashamed
of the things she had said.

They were some distance from the house when a flash of light caught Lisa's eye and, focussing her attention on it, she was surprised to discover a modern swimming pool nestling among tall, shady trees. The water shimmered in the sunlight, almost blinding her, and then a flicker of anxiety stirred within her when she noticed the absence of any sort of protective fencing.

'Can you both swim?' she asked the children at once.

'Yes,' they nodded vigorously, 'but Uncle Adam says the water is still too cold now for us to swim.'

'I should imagine so,' Lisa nodded thoughtfully. 'The days are already getting warmer, but you won't be able to swim for another month or two.'

'Oh, look!' Josh and Kate cried excitedly in unison as they pointed to a grazing camp beyond the pool. 'There are the lambs!'

'Keep the children away from the grazing camps,' Adam Vandeleur's thundering command echoed in her ears as the children rushed towards the fence to watch the woolly merino lambs frolicking in the sun while the ewes continued to graze calmly on what was left of the bushy vegetation.

Lisa hesitated with momentary indecision before following the children. Their uncle would surely not object to their presence if they remained on this side of the fence, she decided firmly, and as she stood there beside them, listening to their exclamations of delight, a newly born lamb ventured inquisitively towards them on unsteady legs. Josh and Kate wriggled their hands through the jackal fencing, encouraging it to come closer, but the lamb retreated nervously, bleating softly as it returned to its anxious mother's side.

Kate tugged at Lisa's skirt. 'Isn't it beautiful, Miss—Miss——'

'Just call me Lisa,' she suggested helpfully.

'Isn't the lamb beautiful, Lisa?' Kate repeated her question, using Lisa's name a little shyly.

'Beautiful,' Lisa agreed readily. 'It looks so soft and silky.'

'There comes Uncle Adam,' Josh exclaimed a little anxiously, and Lisa looked up sharply to see Adam Vandeleur riding across the veld towards them, his body moving in perfect rhythm with the magnificent-looking black stallion beneath him. The animal, like its master, was in perfect physical condition, Lisa thought as she saw the powerful muscles rippling beneath the shiny black coat, but it was the man himself who finally caught and held her rapt attention.

Seated astride that ferocious-looking animal, Adam Vandeleur projected an image of power and ruthless strength and, even at a distance, Lisa could feel the impact of his personality. For some reason she could not explain, this man frightened her, and her body tensed involuntarily when he reined in his horse just beyond the fence. His dark eyes, shaded by the broad rim of his felt hat, gave Lisa no more than a cursory glance, but she felt certain that every detail of her appearance, from the golden sheen of her hair down to her comfortable, low-heeled shoes, had been noted.

There was a strained silence as they waited for him to speak, and when he did, it was Lisa he addressed in that deep, rumbling voice of his.

'The grazing camps are out of bounds, as you very well know, Miss Moreau, so I take it the children are showing you around the farm?'

'Yes, Uncle Adam,' Josh said before Lisa could reply, and then, after a moment of careful deliberation, he asked:

'Uncle Adam, may we hold that baby lamb just for a little while?'

Lisa went cold at Josh's request and stole a quick glance at Adam Vandeleur. It looked for a moment as if he was about to utter a harsh refusal, but then, to her relief, he dismounted, and the lamb was caught swiftly and with a practised ease to be placed gently into Josh's eager little hands.

While the delighted twins took turns to cuddle the lamb, Lisa found herself staring unobtrusively at Adam Vandeleur's hands where they rested comfortably on the wire fence. They were large hands, broad, strong, and well-shaped, with surprisingly clean fingernails. They were hands that could crush without the slightest effort, she thought, and a little shiver of fear made its way up her spine.

She looked away then, trying to concentrate on Josh and Kate, but she was now intensely aware of that tall, imposing figure standing a little more than a metre away from her, and when the children eventually placed the wriggling woolly body in her arms, she felt those dark, piercing eyes scorching and dissecting her until her slight body felt heated and decidedly uncomfortable.

For Lisa it was a unique experience holding a newly born lamb in her arms, but, although her fingers automatically stroked the soft, fleecy body, Adam Vandeleur's presence made it impossible for her to savour the moment as she would have liked to. She handed the lamb back to him across the fence so that it could be returned to the ewe who stood nudging his thigh impatiently and, avoiding the sudden gleam of mockery in his eyes, Lisa hurriedly stepped back a few paces from the fence.

The black stallion tossed its head proudly and pawed

the ground restlessly as Adam Vandeleur swung himself
into the saddle.

'Don't stay out in the sun too long. You haven't got
your hats on,' Adam warned the children, his hands tightening on the reins as the animal quivered with impatience
beneath him. 'I suggest you wear one as well, Miss Moreau,
and if you don't possess a hat, then I suggest you buy one.
The sun in these parts has a deadly sting to it, and the
consequences could be unpleasant.'

He touched his hat briefly, and then horse and rider went
thundering across the veld. Lisa stared after him until he
disappeared beyond a small hill, and then the silence was
broken only by the shrill sound of the cicadas.

'We'd better get back to the house,' she sighed in-
explicably, gesturing the children away from the fence
with her walking-stick. 'It's almost lunch time.'

CHAPTER FOUR

'IT'S our custom, here on the farm, to rest for at least an hour after lunch,' Erica Vandeleur explained to Lisa when they got up from the luncheon table. 'In the summer, when the days are long and hot, you'll appreciate the habit.'

Lisa did not argue with her, and took the twins up to their room. When she closed her own bedroom door behind her some minutes later she found that she was actually thankful for the opportunity to lie down and take the weight off her leg.

With the curtains drawn against the afternoon sun, Lisa lay staring up at the brass canopy of the bed. How quiet it was, she thought as a restful silence settled in and around the house, and then, surprisingly, she knew nothing more until Josh and Kate burst into her room an hour later.

'Did you sleep?' they demanded as they clambered on to her bed and sat there staring at her with those wide, questioning eyes.

Lisa smiled and stifled a yawn. 'I must have done. I remember thinking how quiet it was, and then ... pooff!'

They giggled at her explanation, and then the final remnants of their reserve seemed to vanish. They were all over her now, talking excitedly and simultaneously as they gripped her hands and tried to drag her off the bed, giving her a clear indication that they were in need of a release for their pent-up energy.

For the rest of the afternoon, until it was time for their bath, they showed Lisa no mercy, and although their wild, boisterous games caused Lisa considerable discomfort, she

loved every minute of it. For the first time in months she
found that she could laugh naturally at her own inadequacy
when it came to playing 'Hide and Seek'. She was no match
for Josh and Kate, who could run like wild hares when
she came upon their hiding places, and, consequently, she
did most of the seeking while they hid away in the area
they had marked off for the game.

When the children were eventually put to bed that night,
Lisa soaked her weary body in a hot bath until she felt the
tiredness drain from her limbs. It had, perhaps, been a little
presumptuous of her to think she could cope with two
lively children, and Adam Vandeleur had been perfectly
right to doubt her physical capabilities, she admitted to herself reluctantly while she soaped her body, but she had enjoyed every minute of the day with Josh and Kate, and she
looked forward to the following day. The pain and discomfort would diminish in time, and then ...! The soapy
sponge halted its progress across her shoulder and her
fingers absently traced the scar along her jaw. Surgery
would eventually eliminate the scars, and time might erase
her unsightly limp, but nothing would ever erase the scars
deep down in her soul. In her weakened state of shock,
after learning of Sandy Duncan's death, Rory's horror-filled
eyes had sliced deeply and cruelly, and his silent acceptance when she had returned her ring had killed her frail
hope that his reaction had merely been prompted by concern. He had been only too anxious to leave that stark
white hospital ward with the smell of antiseptics hovering
in the air, and she had watched him go, dry-eyed, and curiously drained of emotion.

The soap slid off the side of the bath and jerked her
back to the present as it splashed into the water. She had
to forget. She *must* forget! she told herself fiercely, and
when she finally went downstairs to dinner there was only

the slightest trace of bitterness about her sensitive mouth.

Adam Vandeleur was not in for dinner that evening either. It had something to do with the inoculation of the sheep which would start the following day, Lisa gathered from his mother. There was also something about three escaped convicts, but Lisa was too relieved at not having to face him across the table to pay much attention to the reason for his absence.

They took their coffee out on to the verandah afterwards, but Erica Vandeleur excused herself and went up to her room when Daisy came out to collect their empty cups. Lisa sat there for a moment longer, drinking in the silent darkness about her, and then a strange restlessness made her wander out into the garden.

It was a beautiful night, and it was good to be alone for a while. With the moon lighting her way, she knew no fear as she walked slowly and aimlessly from the house, relishing the cool breeze that touched her face and arms with a gentleness that was soothing. Half way across the lawn she paused and raised her eyes to the sky. It was odd how bright the stars were in the Karoo, and on this warm, peaceful evening they seemed to be close enough to touch as they glittered in the dark blue velvety sky. It was a night for lovers, she thought ironically, but love was something she no longer believed in ... and no man would want to be the lover of a girl with ...!

'Pull yourself together, Lisa!' she scolded herself loudly as she continued her walk. 'You don't need a man at your side to enjoy the magic of the moonlight.'

Determined to shake off her restlessness, and to rid herself of the dull ache deep down inside of her for which there was no cure, she walked on a little blindly, but, when she reached the trees a few minutes later, she realised that she had walked too far, too fast, and without her walking-stick. Her hip was throbbing, sending stabs of pain into her thigh, and, leaning wearily against the broad stem of the gum tree nearest to her, she eased the weight off her leg and massaged herself gently in an effort to diminish the pain.

How utterly peaceful it was, she thought, closing her eyes and resting heavily against the tree while her hand automatically continued its healing, soothing medication, but the next moment the silence was shattered by the terrifying snarl of an angry animal. Lisa's heart lurched with sickening fear, and her eyes flew open to stare in abject terror at the wolf-like canine storming at her with fangs bared where she stood partially hidden beneath the shadows of the trees. A scream rose to her lips, but it was strangled in her throat, and, closing her eyes tightly, she waited for the moment when the animal's teeth would tear at her flesh.

'Rolf!'

The dog reacted instantly to the sound of that imperious voice, and came to an abrupt halt less than a metre away from Lisa, but even in the darkness she could still see the hair standing erect on its back while it watched her intently and suspiciously.

The numbness of relief surged through her as Adam Vandeleur's tall, dark figure came into her line of vision, but she felt too weak to move, and too perilously close to tears. The beam of a flashlight pierced the moonlit darkness and swept over her briefly, then it was extinguished with a muttered oath that sent a renewed chill of fear through her.

'You're fortunate, Miss Moreau, that I happened to be in the vicinity. Rolf is never very gentle with unwelcome intruders, and that's precisely the reason why I leave him to roam free at night,' that deep, gravelly voice informed her harshly.

'I'm grateful that——'

'Don't move!' His voice, like the sound of a whiplash,

made her freeze in the act of stepping away from the tree. 'The slightest movement and Rolf might again consider you a threat,' he warned, moving closer to her where she stood pinned helplessly to the gum tree, her muscles taut, and hardly daring to breathe, but he made no attempt, as yet, to call off the animal. 'What were you doing out here in the dark?'

The question was shot at her with a suddenness that made her flinch and, disconcerted by the height and breadth of this man towering over her in the darkness, she heard herself stammer foolishly, 'I—I went for a w-walk.'

'Didn't my mother warn you this evening not to stray too far from the house because some escaped convicts are rumoured to be in the neighbourhood?'

Lisa went cold with fright and could have kicked herself for not paying more attention to what Erica Vandeleur had said at the dinner table.

'Your mother did warn me,' she admitted with complete honesty, 'but I'm afraid I—I was thinking of something else at the time, and must have missed that bit about not going too far from the house.'

'You placed yourself in a considerable amount of danger by not heeding my mother's warnings,' his voice lashed her mercilessly in the darkness. 'I received a report, not ten minutes ago, that there's every likelihood that those three armed men are here on my land.'

'I—I'm sorry,' she whispered hoarsely, her eyes wide and frightened at the thought of what might have happened if Adam Vandeleur and his dog had not found her. A tense silence settled between them, a silence broken only by the heavy panting of the dog, and then the stabbing pain in her hip forced her to speak. 'Are—are you going to call off your dog, Mr Vandeleur, or am I to spend the night standing motionless against this tree?'

'It might teach you a lesson you won't soon forget,' he replied cuttingly, with an edge of mockery in his voice. 'It would also be interesting to see how long you could keep it up.'

'No doubt you—find the situation amusing, but I—don't. I——' She gasped, shutting her eyes against the blinding beam of the torch. 'Must you shine that thing directly into my face?'

For a moment the light did not waver from her white, strained face, then it was directed to the ground at her feet, and the dog was instantly called to his side.

'Miss Moreau is a friend, Rolf,' he said, switching off the torch as he spoke, and for a moment Lisa could not see a thing, then her eyes became accustomed to the darkness and she saw the dog shake off his menacing stance only to eye her now with a wary curiosity.

'It doesn't look very much as though he believes you,' she said shakily, not daring to move a muscle until she was certain it was safe for her to do so.

'Stretch out your hand to him, but do it slowly,' her employer instructed her calmly, and she did as she was told while he repeated, 'Friend, Rolf.'

The Alsatian sniffed at her fingers a little warily, then buried his wet nose in the palm of her hand. 'Is it all right for me to stroke him now?'

'That's what he's hoping for,' came the abrupt reply from the man who was nothing but a dark outline in the shadows.

'You're a beautiful dog, Rolf,' Lisa spoke soothingly, but with sincerity as she stroked the smooth head gently.

'Beautiful but dangerous,' Adam Vandeleur warned. 'You needn't fear him again, though.'

Rolf nuzzled her hand in a docile fashion as if to stress his master's statement, but Lisa was hardly aware of him now as she sensed Adam Vandeleur's eyes on her, and it

made her feel decidedly uncomfortable as the silence
lengthened between them. She searched her mind frantically for something to say, but found nothing, and then, as
the mournful howl of a jackal pierced the silence, Adam
Vandeleur moved abruptly.

'I'll see you safely back to the house.'

Lisa accepted his offer in silence and walked beside him
with Rolf following close at their heels. Adam Vandeleur
did not touch her, and neither did he offer her any assistance, but he shortened his long strides to match her slow,
limping gait, and she was thankful to him for this unexpected gesture of consideration.

At the foot of the steps leading up on to the verandah,
Lisa turned to thank him, but the words dried up in her
mouth when her eyes fastened themselves on to those
harsh, rugged features etched so clearly in the moonlight.
What was it about this man that he could rob her of what
little confidence she still had left to reduce her to an in-
significant and stammering idiot? she wondered gravely as
she stared a long way up into those hard eyes glittering so
strangely in the pale light of the moon. There was a powerful aura of masculinity about him that made her feel
ridiculously weak and inadequate. She had experienced
this feeling on the two occasions they had met that morning, and she was experiencing it again now.

'I suggest you go inside, Miss Moreau,' his harsh voice
interrupted her turbulent thoughts. 'Our nights here in the
Karoo can still become chilly at this time of the year.'

It was then, as he turned away from her, that she saw the
lethal-looking weapon slung across his shoulder, and her
eyes widened in dismay.

'You're carrying a rifle,' she stated almost accusingly, an
inexplicable flicker of anxiety loosening her tongue. 'You're
not going to try and catch those convicts on your own, are
you?'

'Not on my own, no.' There was mockery in every hard line of his face as he turned back to her, but there was also a hint of something else she could not define. 'That jackal you heard howling a few minutes ago was a signal from one of my labourers to let me know they think they've spotted something.'

'Do—do you think they're armed? The convicts, I mean?'

'I know they're armed,' he stated quietly and decisively, then he gestured impatiently with the hand that held the torch. 'Go inside, Miss Moreau, and lock the front door behind you.'

Lisa felt as though she was being strangled slowly but surely, and she asked stupidly, 'How—how will you get in?'

'I have the key to the back door,' he said, and then mockery curved that hard mouth into the suggestion of a smile when she still hesitated. 'There's no need for you to fear anything, Miss Moreau. The house will be patrolled all night, or until the danger has passed.'

'It's not *myself* I'm afraid for, but I'm afraid for *you*!' the words seemed to leap from the hidden and mysterious depths of her soul, but they never passed her lips, for she bit them back with a horrified gasp.

'Goodnight, Mr Vandeleur,' she managed somehow and, without looking back, she entered the house and locked the door behind her as he had instructed.

She was shaking so much that she could hardly climb the stairs, but she stubbornly refused to analyse the reason for her startling thoughts. She banished the entire incident from her mind and went to bed, but she was still awake when she heard the low murmur of voices beneath her window well after midnight.

She was out of bed in a flash and, although the verandah roof obscured her vision, she could not deny her relief when she recognised Adam Vandeleur's voice amidst those of his labourers. Judging by the animated tone of their lowered voices, their efforts had been successful, and only then did Lisa go to sleep, to have Erica Vandeleur confirm, at the breakfast table the following morning, that Adam and his men had caught the convicts without suffering any casualties.

As the weeks passed and lengthened into a month, Lisa made every effort to stay out of Adam Vandeleur's way as much as possible. He was far too disturbing, and much too aggressively masculine for her to ever feel at ease in his company, and between them there was also the knowledge that he had considered her incapable of looking after the twins.

Despite all her initial misgivings, Lisa had settled down quickly to this new way of life. The fresh air and the long daily walks with the twins had strengthened her hip to the extent that she no longer needed her walking-stick, and, as she relaxed on her bed one afternoon towards the end of that first month on the farm, her thoughts turned involuntarily to Josh and Kate resting in the room next to her own. They had accepted their new routine without a murmur of protest, and their behaviour had been almost impeccable, while at the same time they had attached themselves to Lisa with a fierce fondness which she had found a little frightening at times. It was almost as if they had found in Lisa the mother they had lost, and this perturbed her very much.

Erica Vandeleur frequently entertained visitors from the neighbouring farms, but the most frequent visitor was Willa Jackson, who came and went more or less as if she knew the place would one day belong to her. Tall and slender, with thick auburn hair hanging straight down on to her shoulders, she won Lisa's admiration for her undeniable knowledge of sheep farming. Willa was undoubtedly extremely capable, but this in no way detracted from her femininity. She was beautiful, but cold, Lisa discovered on closer acquaintance, however, but she also decided that Willa was exactly the right kind of wife for a hard-bitten farmer like Adam Vandeleur—*if* he should choose to marry her.

Once, when Willa had joined them for afternoon tea in the garden, Lisa had seen Adam's eyes dwelling on the beautiful, unscarred face of the girl lounging in the chair beside his own, and it had filled Lisa with the most peculiar feeling of despondency. Thinking of it now, she could still not explain to herself why she should have felt that way, and, turning over on to her side, she allowed herself to be lulled by the restful silence in the house.

Lisa slept for almost an hour before she awoke with the feeling that something was wrong. Josh and Kate were not in their room, she discovered a few moments later, and, after a fruitless search of the house and the garden, Lisa was forced to seek the assistance of Erica Vandeleur's most trusted servant.

'Have you seen the children anywhere?' Lisa questioned Daisy when she found her in the kitchen giving her usual care and attention to the evening meal.

'No, Miss Lisa.' Daisy closed the oven door and straightened, a frown on her face as she turned to Lisa. 'They're not in their room?'

'No.' Lisa felt her stomach muscles tightening with anxiety. With only a few days to go before her probationary period expired, she could imagine Adam Vandeleur's cutting remarks if anything untoward happened, and she could no longer reject the suspicion that was thrusting its way to the surface of her mind. She had overheard the twins discussing an old well on the farm and, precipitating their

natural tendency to explore, she had warned them severely
to stay away, but their sudden disappearance was beginning
to imply that they had ignored her warning. 'Daisy, if the
children wanted to get hold of some rope, where would
they find it?'

'Rope, Miss Lisa?' Daisy's eyes were wide and questioning, but at the look of impatience on Lisa's face, she said
quickly, 'There's a rope hanging up against the wall on the
back stoep.'

A hasty inspection revealed nothing but a leather thong
draped carelessly over the hook and, cutting across the
woman's exclamation of surprise, Lisa said hurriedly,
'There's a disused well somewhere on this farm. Do you
know where it is?'

'Yes, Miss Lisa. It's just otherside that hill you see there,'
Daisy replied, pointing to the brush-covered hill beyond
the shearing shed. 'It's not very far.'

'Thank you.'

'Miss Lisa?' Daisy's voice sliced anxiously through the
afternoon silence. 'Do you think the children have gone
there?'

'I think they may have, but——' Lisa raised her finger to
her lips in a silencing gesture, 'not a word to anyone until
I've made sure.'

Daisy nodded mutely, and Lisa shot up a silent prayer as
she set off in search of the twins.

It seemed to take an eternity before she reached that
particular hill, but it had, in fact, taken her less than ten
minutes to get there. Her breath was rasping in her throat,
however, and her heart was thudding painfully against her
ribs when she paused for a moment on the crest of the
hill, but something red caught her attention, and her
heart leapt into her throat as she recognised Kate's crouch-
ing figure beside what was obviously a gaping hole in the

ground. With a total disregard for the stabbing pain in her hip, Lisa almost ran down the other side of the hill.

'Lisa, Lisa, come quickly!' Kate's anxious little voice spurred her on, and a few seconds later Lisa was on her knees beside the child, clutching her tightly in her arms.

'Where's Josh?' Lisa asked unnecessarily, for a rope was tied inexpertly but firmly to the stem of an old thorn tree. Her horrified glance followed it down the hole, and from deep within the bowels of the well a whimpering sound confirmed her worst fears.

'His h-hands slipped on the rope, and he f-fell,' Kate explained sobbingly, but Lisa was already lying flat on her stomach and peering down into the darkness.

'Josh, can you hear me?' Lisa questioned sharply, her eyes seeking out the little body huddled more than five metres down on the floor of the well.

'Yes, Lisa ... I can hear you,' Josh's voice floated up towards her.

'Have you hurt yourself?'

'I bashed my head a little, and my hand is scratched, and I can't stand on my foot.' A stifled sob reached her ears and tore at her heart. 'Lisa, get me out ... please!'

'Can you reach the rope?'

'No, it's too high.'

Close to despair, and much as Lisa disliked the idea, there was only one thing left to do and, getting to her feet, she took Kate firmly by the shoulders and prayed that the child would do as she was told.

'I want you to listen very carefully, Kate. Go back to the house and tell Daisy exactly what happened. Ask her to send for your uncle, and she's to tell him to bring a longer rope with him. When you've done that, you're to stay at the house, do you understand?'

Kate nodded tearfully. 'Yes, Lisa.'

'Off you go, then,' Lisa smiled at her with as much re-assurance as she could manage, giving her a gentle push in the direction of the homestead.

'Lisa, where are you?' Josh demanded anxiously the moment Kate had gone.

'I'm here, Josh,' she called to him reassuringly while she retied the rope around the tree-trunk, then, testing it to make sure that it would take her weight, she swung her legs over the edge of the well. 'I'm coming down to you.'

'You'll fall!'

'No, I won't,' Lisa insisted, thinking that it was just as well that she was wearing her old denims and sensible shoes. She was grateful, too, for the experience she had gained when, as a student, she had gone on several expeditions up into the mountains, and using her feet as leverage against the rough sides of the well, she climbed down carefully, but the musty stench almost succeeded in taking her breath away before her feet touched the bottom. Josh, trembling and whimpering softly, was in her arms the next instant, and Lisa pacified him, waiting until his tears ceased before she held him a little away from her. 'Let's have a look at you.'

The late afternoon sun sent a slanted shaft of light into the opening of the well, but it was sufficient for her to see the bump on his forehead, and the streaks of dirt on his face and clothes. His hand was fortunately only grazed, but his badly sprained ankle was obviously causing him considerable discomfort, for he winced when her fingers gently explored the swollen areas.

It was difficult working in such a confined space, but as she set about tearing a strip off the bottom of her old cotton blouse in order to utilise it as a bandage, she heard Josh say tearfully, 'I'm sorry, Lisa.'

'Yes, I know.'

'Are you very cross with me for not listening to you?'

'I *should* be very cross with you,' Lisa admitted, 'but there'll be time enough for that later.'

Leaving his shoe on for added support, she strapped up his ankle with the improvised bandage, and Josh watched her in silence for a while before he asked: 'How are we going to get out of here?'

'I can't get you out on my own, so we're just going to sit here quietly and wait for your uncle to come and help us.'

'Uncle Adam's going to be very cross.'

'I should imagine so,' Lisa replied with an outward calmness, but as she tied off the bandage she felt her insides quaking at the thought of Adam Vandeleur's anger. 'Does that feel any better?'

Josh nodded silently and, slipping her arm about him, she held him against her with his head resting on her shoulder while they waited for help to arrive.

It was an agonising wait, with plenty of time to come to terms with the certain knowledge that Adam Vandeleur would not pass up this opportunity to dismiss her from his service. Lisa had grown fond of the children, and leaving them would be more painful than she had imagined, but, when the earth finally vibrated with the sound of approaching horses, she had prepared herself for the inevitable.

Josh glanced up at Lisa anxiously when the pounding hooves ceased to shake the earth around them, and she summoned a reassuring smile which she hoped would look convincing. A horse snorted impatiently somewhere above them, and then Adam Vandeleur's deep, thundering voice echoed down the well.

'*Miss Moreau? Are you down there?*'

CHAPTER FIVE

'ARE you down there, Miss Moreau?'

Lisa swallowed hard before shouting back, 'Yes, I am.'

Adam muttered something she was thankful she could not hear from down there, and then those ruggedly chiselled features came into her line of vision. 'Are you all right?'

'Yes, I'm all right.'

'And Josh?'

'A bit battered, but he's okay.'

'Good.' Adam disappeared from view, and a soft whining noise made her realise that Rolf was up there with his master, and probably just as anxious about what had happened. 'Look, I'm lowering a longer rope,' Adam said when he returned to the opening above them. 'There's a noose at the end of it. Slip it round Josh's waist, will you?'

The rope was lowered, but Lisa was unable to think or feel, as she helped Josh to his feet and fastened the noose firmly about his waist. Later, perhaps, the nightmare quality of the situation would affect her, but right now Josh, wide-eyed and frightened, needed her love and reassurance, and she gave it to him unstintingly and calmly.

'Have you got the rope around him?' Adam demanded of Lisa.

'Yes.'

'Can you hang on to the rope, Josh, so it doesn't tighten too much around your waist?'

'I—I'll try, Uncle Adam,' the child said unsteadily, clutching at the rope.

'Right!' Adam issued an abrupt command to someone

standing beside him, and then his tall figure appeared at the opening of the well once more. 'I'm going to pull you up now, Josh.'

Lisa stood with bated breath and watched the child being raised slowly to the surface. He was almost out, her heart rejoiced, and then he panicked suddenly.

'The rope's slipping, Uncle Adam!' he cried.

'Just hang on as tight as you can. I've nearly got you,' Adam ordered sharply, and a few seconds later Josh disappeared over the edge to the accompaniment of Rolf's excited barking, and then Lisa heard Adam say: 'Take care of Josh, Petrus.'

Now it was *her* turn, Lisa realised nervously. Climbing down into the well had been reasonably easy, but going up would be a little more difficult, and she only hoped her leg would not cave in under her weight.

'I'm lowering the rope for you, Miss Moreau. Fasten it around your waist.' He waited a few moments, then demanded, 'Have you done that?'

Lisa licked her dry lips. 'Yes.'

'Use your feet as leverage against the side of the well, if you can,' he instructed her unnecessarily, and then she felt the rope grow taut beneath her hands. 'Ready?'

'Ready!' she called back.

The rope bit into her waist just above the belt of her denims where her skin had been bared after tearing a strip off her blouse, and, in her attempt to ease the pressure, she lost her foothold against the side of the well. Her body swung forward, and, as her left hip made contact with a jutting stone, a sharp, agonising pain shot from her hip down into her thigh. She could not prevent herself from crying out, and the process of pulling her up was instantly halted.

'What's wrong? What's happened?' Adam demanded.

'Nothing,' she gasped, momentarily blinded by the pain and gritting her teeth against the flow of tears. 'Just pull me up.'

A few seconds, or was it hours later, she heard Rolf barking once more, but he was silenced sharply as strong hands lifted her clear, and then the smell of the sun, the veld, and tobacco mingled, quivering in her nostrils and attacking her senses as she found herself reclining weakly against a broad, muscular chest. Her hands encountered the roughness of soft, springy hair where the top buttons of his shirt had come undone, and her heart felt as though it was pounding in her mouth when she stared up into that granite-like face just above her own.

It was not the first time Adam had touched her, but now, lying in his arms like this, it felt as though she had been wired up to several volts of electricity, and the current that surged through her body was unlike anything she had ever experienced before.

'Did you hurt yourself?' his voice vibrated along her sensitive nerves.

'My—my foot slipped, and I—I jarred my hip, but I—I'm all right now.'

'Are you sure?'

'Yes—yes, I'm sure,' she assured him in breathless haste when she felt the disturbing touch of one large, strong hand exploring her hip and thigh. 'It's Josh you should look at.'

Adam's lips twisted with faint derision, then he released her and turned to Josh who sat silently and miserably beside Petrus, Adam's foreman. Adam examined the child's injuries thoroughly before sitting back on his heels and fastening his stern glance on the boy.

'Well, Josh? I think you have some explaining to do.'

'I—I didn't think anything would happen, and we just

wanted to see what was in the well,' Josh explained, his bottom lip quivering faintly. 'I'm sorry, Uncle Adam.'

Adam swung round and Lisa experienced the force of those dark eyes pinning her to the dry, dusty earth. 'Was this your idea of an afternoon excursion, Miss Moreau?'

Lisa grew hot under his disparaging glance and stammered, 'I—well, I——'

'It wasn't Lisa's fault, Uncle Adam,' Josh interrupted, surprising Lisa into silence.

'Who gave you permission to call Miss Moreau by her name?'

'I gave the children permission,' Lisa intervened weakly, and once again his disturbing attention was focussed on her.

'It isn't her fault, Uncle Adam,' Josh defended Lisa with childish determination. 'She—she told us not to climb down the well, but——'

'But you deliberately disobeyed her,' Adam filled in for the child with a harsh note in his voice that made Josh flinch visibly.

'Yes,' Josh admitted bravely, his lips quivering as he raised anxious eyes to his uncle's. 'Are you going to—to smack me, Uncle Adam?'

The shrill sound of the cicadas became almost deafening during the tense silence that followed, and then Adam rose to his feet and shook his dark head slowly.

'I think you've been punished enough, and you're very lucky you haven't broken any bones.'

Lisa expelled the air slowly from her lungs and got to her feet unsteadily, her hand stroking the Alsatian's smooth head absently when he brushed up against her. Josh had got off lightly, she thought as she watched Adam lifting the child on to Petrus's horse, but she was certain he would not show the same leniency towards her for allowing this incident to occur.

With Josh safely in Petrus's care, Adam took hold of the reins of his horse and turned towards Lisa. When those dark, penetrating eyes met hers, she knew exactly what he was about to suggest, and she shrank inwardly from the idea.

'I—I'll walk,' she forestalled him.

'With a hip that's giving you hell?' Adam demanded harshly.

'My hip isn't giving me—hell—as you put it.'

'Then why are you massaging it like that?'

To her utter dismay Lisa discovered that she was doing exactly that, and she removed her hand instantly, avoiding the mockery in his eyes. 'It's ... habit, I suppose.'

'Really?' he remarked sarcastically, swinging himself up into the saddle, but Lisa did not stay to argue with him, and started limping up the hill in the direction of the homestead.

She should have realised that Adam was not the kind to be easily thwarted, for he swerved his horse towards her, and her horrified gasp was rudely stifled when his hard arm was latched about her waist, almost squeezing the breath from her lungs as he lifted her up in front of him on to the horse's back.

'This wasn't necessary,' she protested weakly. 'I'm not——'

'Shut up!' he growled in her ear. 'And relax, will you, or it's going to be an uncomfortable ride for both of us.'

Lisa did as she was told while Adam gestured Petrus on ahead with the child, and then, as Adam dug his heels into the horse's flanks, Lisa experienced for the first time the thrill of being seated on the back of such a powerful animal. It would have been a most enjoyable ride except for her intense awareness of the man seated behind her. His hard chest was against her shoulder, and his breath was warm against her cheek, but what disturbed her most was the touch of that warm, work-roughened hand against her bare flesh where she had ripped her blouse away. His touch seemed to scorch her, and while her blood began to flow more swiftly through her veins, her nerves were sending frantic little messages to her brain; messages that made no sense at that moment except to fill her with alarm.

Neither of them spoke during the short ride to the homestead, but pandemonium broke loose when they finally arrived at the house. Erica Vandeleur, Daisy and Kate seemed to bundle out of the kitchen door simultaneously, but it was the children's grandmother who spoke first.

'What happened?' she demanded, her anxious glance taking in Lisa's dishevelled appearance and Josh's dirty countenance as they were lifted off the horses.

'Get the children upstairs and into a bath while I do the explaining,' Adam ordered Lisa bluntly. 'I'll be up later to strap up that ankle of Josh's.'

With Daisy's help, Lisa managed to get the twins upstairs and into the bath. They were unnaturally subdued while Lisa and Daisy scrubbed them clean and put on their pyjamas, but when Adam walked into their room a half hour later, the twins went a definite shade paler. It was obvious that they expected some kind of retribution for their disobedience, but when none seemed to be forthcoming, Lisa suspected that Josh and Kate found Adam's silence just as frightening as she did.

Adam placed the first-aid box on the floor beside the bed and, after re-examining Josh's ankle very carefully, he applied an ointment to the affected area, and strapped it up expertly with a clean crêpe bandage.

All this was done with surprising gentleness, and when he finally straightened, his eyes travelled with deliberate slowness over Lisa. It was then that she realised what a bedraggled mess she herself must be, and embarrassment sent a wave of colour surging up into her cheeks. His ruthless mouth twisted a little cynically and humorously as if he enjoyed her discomfiture, and then he was gone, leaving behind only the force of his personality which was frightening enough even in his absence.

Daisy, thankfully, took charge of the twins, and, alone in her bedroom a few moments later, Lisa took a capsule for the nagging pain in her hip, and stared at herself in the mirror with something akin to horror.

There was dust in her hair and a streak of dirt across her nose. Her denims were soiled and her blouse, or what was left of it, only just succeeded in covering her breasts. She looked a sight, she thought with a grimace, and while running her bath water, she stripped down to the skin and disposed of her dirty clothes.

The hot bath did wonders for her aching hip, but it did nothing for her nervousness at the confrontation which was yet to come between Adam Vandeleur and herself, and, as she wrapped a towel around her wet hair, she could almost hear that harsh voice of his dismissing her.

Dressed, later, in an old tweed skirt with a green, long-sleeved blouse, Lisa took a little time with her make-up before she brushed her fine, silky hair until it shone like gold. She looked cool and confident, she decided as she stared at her image in the mirror, but deep down inside she was afraid; afraid of facing Adam and afraid of what he would say.

A quick glance at her wristwatch told her that she could no longer prolong the inevitable and, squaring her slim shoulders, she went downstairs to find Erica Vandeleur already seated at the one end of the long oak table. She smiled warmly at Lisa, banishing a little of the chilliness about her heart, but heavy footsteps approaching the dining-room made Lisa's answering smile freeze on her lips.

As always, Adam's presence had a startling effect on her nervous system, but on this occasion her pulse rate quickened alarmingly when he walked into the room. She recalled the way she had lain weakly against his chest, and felt again the hard pressure of that tanned, muscular arm about her waist as she had felt it during that uncomfortable ride back to the homestead, and her cheeks flared hotly at the memory.

Adam, however, gave her nothing but a cursory glance as he pulled out his chair and sat down, and his silent, almost morose attitude during dinner shattered the remaining fragments of hope she had clung to so desperately.

Lisa tried to concentrate on her food, but she hardly knew what she was eating, so intensely aware was she of every movement Adam made, and of the muscles rippling beneath his clean white cotton shirt. His powerful body suggested a limitless strength and stamina that was awe-inspiring, and also a little frightening, but it was the unrelenting line of his jaw that troubled her most. Adam Vandeleur would not overlook this incident, and she was convinced that he took a cruel delight in stretching out the inevitable. She would be dismissed without a flicker of regret, and she was becoming more certain of this with every second that passed.

When Adam retired to his study after dinner, Lisa excused herself from the table and went up to her room. She paced the floor restlessly, expecting at any moment to be summoned to his study, but, as the hours passed, nothing happened, and she went to bed eventually, still nursing her anxiety.

Sleep evaded her, and the silent darkness made her increasingly aware of an inexplicable weight in her chest. Her breathing became laboured, her palms damp with perspiration as she lived again through the frightening experience of finding Josh at the bottom of the disused well, and suddenly she could not stand being cooped up in the confines of her room a minute longer. She needed a breath of fresh air, but more than that, she needed peace of mind. The latter would be a little difficult to obtain, but fresh air was no problem, and, slipping out of bed, she put on her gown and went downstairs, the soft mules on her feet making no sound as she crossed the spacious entrance hall with its antique furniture. The old grandfather clock ticked away the seconds as she fumbled in the darkness to unlock the front door, and moments later she stepped out on to the verandah to draw the cool, fresh night air deep into her tortured lungs.

The brilliance of the stars never ceased to fascinate her, and she tried, foolishly, to count them as she leaned against the wooden rails. The night was no longer silent, for the insects in the undergrowth loudly chorused their own particular brand of noise, but to Lisa, at that moment, it was like music, primitive and exciting. Shutting her mind to the turmoil of her thoughts, she lost herself in the scented darkness of her surroundings, at peace, for a time, until something alerted her to the realisation that she was not alone.

Rolf, the Alsatian, bounded up the steps and padded softly towards her to nudge her thigh fondly. They were no longer strangers to each other and, as Lisa's hand fondled the smooth head, she knew that Adam would not be far behind. Her body tensed when she picked up the faint aroma of cigarette smoke and, conscious suddenly of being dressed only in her night attire, she fled towards the door, but Adam emerged from the shadows at that precise moment to bar her way.

Tall and broad, he towered over her frighteningly, and

she shrank from him instinctively until she felt the roughness of the wall digging into her back. She could not see his face, only the outline of his arrogant, proudly held head, but she felt his dark, penetrating gaze making use of the moonlight to take in every part of her now trembling body as she cowered against the wall.

'What the devil are you doing out here at this time of night?'

The deep, resonant timbre of his voice sent a peculiar little shiver along her nervous system, and she stammered like a child caught in the act of doing something unforgivable. 'I—I couldn't sleep, so I—I came out for a breath of—of fresh air.'

'Is your hip giving you trouble?'

'No.' He was so close to her now that she could detect the clean, fresh smell of the veld as it clung to him, and all at once her wary heart was beating in her throat. This was the moment she had dreaded, but, unable to stand the uncertainty a moment longer, she stumblingly brought matters to a head. 'I suppose that—that after what happened this afternoon you—you want me to leave Fairview.'

'Why should I want that?'

Was he mocking her? she wondered confusedly as she said : 'I should have guessed what the twins were planning, especially after hearing them discuss the well, and I should have been a little more observant, but instead I ... was asleep.'

'It's impossible for anyone to keep a twenty-four-hour watch on the children, and you did warn them not to go near the well.'

Lisa's heart skipped a beat as she asked with breathless incredulity, 'Do you mean you—you don't blame me?'

A low rumble of unexpected laughter seemed to come from deep within his throat. 'You sound unconvinced.'

'Well, I—you weren't too keen to take me on in the first

place,' she explained haltingly, totally confused and be-wildered by his attitude. 'That's why I—I thought——'

'You thought I was waiting for an opportunity, like this one for instance, to send you packing?' he finished for her quietly.

'Something like that ... yes,' she admitted, her cheeks growing hot.

He moved suddenly in the darkness, and then his hand was warm and rough against her cheek. The unexpected-ness of it startled her into immobility and left her speechless as she felt his fingers against the scar above her left temple, then he deliberately explored the scar running from ear to chin. His touch on the raised, sensitive skin was electrify-ing, and there was a sudden clamouring in her body which she could not understand. She held her breath, too afraid to move, and then she was overwhelmed by the knowledge that here was one man who was obviously not repulsed by her scars in the least.

'Is that why you couldn't sleep? Because you thought I was going to send you away?'

He lowered his hand to his side as he spoke, but she was still under the spell of his touch. She stared up at him in a dazed fashion for several moments before she understood what he was referring to, and, colouring swiftly, she said lamely, 'I've grown very fond of the twins.'

'Not many women would have climbed down into the stench of an old well to sit with an injured child until help arrived, so forget what I said about being on probation.' There was just the slightest hint of praise in his voice, but it sent the blood flowing warmly through her veins as he added forcefully: 'You're staying.'

'Thank you,' she whispered unsteadily, making an effort to pull herself together. 'About that well ...'

'The well will be sealed off properly this time,' he told her with his usual abruptness, and turned away from her, his attitude conveying his dismissal of her even before he spoke. 'Goodnight, Lisa.'

'Goodnight, Mr Vandeleur.'

Her voice had sounded prim, almost detached, but all she could think of as she arduously climbed the stairs up to her room was the sound of her name on Adam Vandeleur's lips. He had called her Lisa, probably without even realising it, but it had given her the strangest thrill of pleasure to hear him do so.

She was being ridiculous, she told herself sternly. It was relief at the discovery that she was not to be dismissed from his service that made her feel this way, but she felt again the rough warmth of his hand against her cool cheek, and it was the memory of that touch that finally made her go to sleep with a smile on her lips.

Josh's resilience was remarkable. Within less than a week after falling down that old well, he was running about with as much enthusiasm as his sister. The nightmare incident was forgotten, and Lisa once again had her hands full trying to keep the twins in order.

'Don't let them tire you too much,' Erica Vandeleur warned when Lisa joined her for tea on the verandah one morning after one of those mad ball games on the lawn with Josh and Kate.

'I don't mind,' Lisa sighed, flushed and happy as she leaned back in the cane chair and sipped her tea. 'I enjoy the exercise, and it's done wonders for me despite being a little painful at times.'

'I've noticed you seem to be walking better,' the older woman observed, her warm glance taking in the small slenderness of the girl in the chair opposite her. 'Are you happy here with us, Lisa?'

'Oh, yes, very happy,' Lisa replied without hesitation.

'It's not as primitive, then, as you imagined it would be?'

Lisa almost choked on a mouthful of tea, and her cheeks reddened as she met Erica Vandeleur's humorous glance.

'I suppose you've heard from my Aunt Molly,' she observed weakly, and Mrs Vandeleur nodded laughingly.

'I had a letter from her a few days ago, and she was very concerned about you. She mentioned your doubts about living under such ...' that teasing smile flashed again, '... primitive conditions.'

Lisa coloured again, but as she placed her empty cup in the tray she tried to explain. 'I had no idea what it would be like to live on a sheep farm, and as I'd never done anything other than teach before, I very much doubted that I was capable of looking after two small children. I had very little confidence in myself at the time, and Adam—Mr Vandeleur,' she corrected herself hastily, 'had very little confidence in my suitability as well.'

Erica Vandeleur frowned. 'Adam no longer feels that way, I'm sure. Why, just the other day he said the children have never been as well-behaved as they have been since your arrival.'

The sun was suddenly brighter on that warm October morning, and a strange new happiness surged through her; a happiness that did odd things to her pulse rate and then left her wondering at the reason for it. Why should the slightest compliment from Adam make her feel as though she was walking on air? Most of the time he treated her as if she did not exist, while she ...!

Lisa drew her breath in sharply, oblivious of the older woman's speculative glance. It was ridiculous and quite out of the question. She did not even *like* her employer. He was always so disturbingly frightening, and yet ...

'You've gone quite pale, Lisa. Are you all right?'

At the sound of Erica Vandeleur's voice Lisa came to her senses, and, admonishing herself silently for her wild flight of fancy, she said: 'I'm quite all right, thank you, but I think I should go and see what the children are up to.'

Erica Vandeleur nodded silently, but Lisa could feel her anxious eyes following her as she went in search of Josh and Kate.

It took Lisa a considerable time to rid herself of the alarming thoughts which had taken shape in her mind that morning, and she had almost succeeded in forgetting the incident when a small flat parcel was brought up to her room before dinner that evening. The lilac wrapping gave her no indication as to the origin and contents of the parcel, but her hands were trembling when she finally lifted the lid of the flat box to find her name written boldly on a small envelope inside. She knew that handwriting; she had seen it on the cheque Adam had given her at the end of the previous month, and her heart began to thud uncomfortably as she extracted the card.

Accept this as a replacement for the one you were forced to discard.   A.V.

Lisa knew at once what it was and, lifting the tissue paper, she encountered a blouse made of the finest, most exquisite silk, with its wide collar embroidered in satin, and its long sleeves gathered in at the cuffs.

Touched by this gesture from a man whom she knew could be gentle, as well as a hard, unfeeling brute, she allowed herself the luxury of holding the blouse up against her while she admired herself in the mirror. It was the most beautiful thing she had ever seen, and the desire to try it on was very strong, but she could not accept it, she realised a little sadly as she returned it carefully to its box. Her fingers caressed the material lovingly, almost longingly, but her soft mouth became set with determination as she went downstairs to join Adam and his mother at the dinner table.

CHAPTER SIX

LISA was a little nervous at the dinner table that evening, but the meal progressed in the usual manner with Adam saying very little, except to answer his mother's occasional queries, and Lisa began to wonder just why she had imagined he would behave differently. In no way did he give any indication that he had had anything to do with that beautiful gift which she had left on her bed in readiness to return to him, and, if it was not for the note addressed to her in his own handwriting, she would seriously have doubted his involvement.

Adam did not stay to have coffee on the verandah with Lisa and his mother, but excused himself and went through to his study and, when Mrs Vandeleur finally went up to her room, Lisa decided to risk Adam's wrath. His study was forbidden territory when he was there, she had learnt, but Lisa felt certain that the circumstances warranted this interruption.

With her nerves tightening into a knot at the pit of her stomach, she knocked on the study door a few seconds later and, at his abrupt command, she went in and closed the door softly behind her. Adam's pen halted its progress across the sheet of paper in front of him, and there was a faint look of surprise on his face when he looked up, but then his eyes seemed to burn right through her with an intensity that made her flinch inwardly.

She expected a ruthless reprimand, but when he merely continued to stare at her in that silent, brooding fashion, she asked hesitantly, 'May I—speak to—to you for a moment, please?'

'Is it important?' he barked, his heavy eyebrows drawing together in à frown.

'It is to me, yes.'

He did not invite her to sit down, and she stood with her hands clutched tightly behind her back, shifting her weight uncomfortably from one foot to the other as he snapped, 'Go ahead, then.'

Completely disconcerted by his manner, her mind went frighteningly blank for a few seconds, but the hardening of his rugged features acted as a spur and she hastily pulled herself together.

'I—I would like to thank you for the blouse you've given me, but ...'

'But?' he prompted harshly when her voice faded on her.

'As a replacement it's—it's far too expensive for me to accept.'

There was a deathly silence in the study, and then she flinched nervously as he dropped his pen on to the blotter and rose to his feet. With his hands pushed deep into the pockets of his corduroy pants, he walked round his desk to stand facing her, and the height and breadth of him dwarfed her so completely that, not for the first time, she wished herself a couple of centimetres taller.

'I don't usually have my gifts thrown back in my face,' he announced with displeasure in every syllable he uttered.

'Oh, please—I'm not—it's just that——'

'Is it the wrong size?' he probed harshly.

'Oh, no.'

'Does the style not appeal to you?'

'No, no! It's beautiful, but——'

Lisa bit her lip, aware that she not only felt like an idiot but that she was behaving like one too. Adam was making it extremely difficult for her to explain her reasons for not accepting his gift, and to have him towering over her like this made matters worse. He was much too close for comfort and, with her eyes on a level with the hard wall of his chest, she could not help remembering the feel of him, and the warm male smell of him when she had lain weakly against him after being dragged from the well. Her heart-beats quickened erratically at the memory, and she took an involuntary pace away from him in an effort to steady herself, but her action merely evoked his mockery, as if he was well aware of the effect he was beginning to have on her.

'Are you afraid I might demand some sort of payment for my ... generosity?'

A shiver of shock went through Lisa, and her eyes widened with alarm as she raised them to his. 'Oh, no! I never thought that at all. Besides, you're not—not——'

'Yes?' he prompted, his mouth twisting derisively when she came to an embarrassed stop, and her cheeks were suddenly on fire.

'You're not the kind of man who would bargain with gifts in order to—to get what you want,' she managed finally, but she could not look him in the eyes, and fastened her glance instead on the silver buckle attached to the broad leather belt at his slim waist.

Their conversation had all at once become too dangerous, and much too personal. It had awakened her to a sensual awareness of him as a man, and she dared not think of him as anything else but her employer.

'You're quite right,' his voice vibrated along her receptive nerves, but there was an element of danger in the air that placed her instantly on the alert as he added darkly: 'What I want ... I take. Like *this*, for instance.'

Lisa had been prepared for a verbal battle with Adam

Vandeleur, but she was totally unprepared for the force
with which her body made contact with his. His arms were
locked about her smallness like a painful vice, and her
startled gasp was smothered beneath the ruthless demand
of lips that showed no mercy in the violation of her mouth.
She was released again after a few seconds with an equally
staggering swiftness, and the room spun crazily about her
as she clutched wildly at the desk for support while Adam
returned to his chair as if nothing had happened.

'You may do what you like with my gift,' he announced
in a tone of dismissal as he picked up his pen. 'I have no
further interest in the matter.'

Conscious of the fact that she was shaking in every limb,
and of a soaring in her ears that made her feel as though
she was on the verge of fainting, Lisa somehow reached
the door and wrenched it open. She could not recall afterwards whether she had closed it behind her or not, for the
only conscious thought in her mind at that time was to get
away from Adam Vandeleur, and as quickly as possible before she humiliated herself utterly and completely by burst-
ing into tears.

Later, when the shock of what had occurred no longer
had such a devastating effect on her, she tried to find an
answer for Adam's unpredictable behaviour, but could not.
She could still feel the hard impact of his mouth on her
bruised lips, and a tremor shook through her as she recalled
her quick, involuntary response. It had been a ruthless kiss,
but it had shaken her to the very depths of her being as no
other man's kisses had ever done before. Rory had kissed
her many times and, thinking herself in love with him at
that time, she had enjoyed his kisses—she had, in fact,
yearned for them—but never had his kisses affected her as
much as that one, passionless kiss from Adam Vandeleur
had done.

It frightened her now to think of it, but her mind clung relentlessly to those startling moments in the arms of a man who had filled her with an inexplicable wariness from the moment they had met. She had sensed the danger then, and she was even more strongly aware of it now. He could be gentle—she had discovered that when he had attended to Josh's ankle—but he could also be cruelly harsh, and frighteningly brutal if he wished, and it was this side of her employer's character that she feared most.

Lisa picked up the box with its lilac wrapping and thrust it into the furthest corner of her wardrobe. She wanted to forget about Adam's unexpected, and unacceptable gift, but the memory of what had transpired in his study would not be erased that easily.

'What I want ... I take,' he had said, and he had taken her lips to draw from them a startling response that even now confused her, making her realise that she would have to be infinitely more careful in future not to let it happen again.

It was impossible to avoid someone when you lived under the same roof with them, Lisa discovered during the next few days, and, with the arrival of the manager Adam had employed for Waverley, his late brother's farm, Lisa found it even more difficult to give her employer a wide berth. He began to spend increasingly more time on his own property and, to Lisa's dismay, she seemed to encounter Adam wherever she went with the twins. He was seldom alone, however, for Willa Jackson was always close at hand, and her possessiveness was beginning to make it obvious to Lisa that this woman intended becoming the mistress of Adam's kingdom. She seldom made an effort to speak to Lisa, for it was as if she considered it beneath her dignity to do more than acknowledge the presence of a mere employee, but her green eyes continually flashed a warning at Lisa to keep her distance from Adam. It was a source of secret amusement to Lisa that Willa should consider her a threat, for Adam Vandeleur was not at all the kind of man who would interest her in that way, but Willa was obviously not taking any chances.

Kenneth Rudman, the new manager, came to dinner one evening at Erica Vandeleur's invitation. He was a lean young man with unruly brown hair and hungry eyes, but his knowledge and efficiency in farming was unquestionable, and on the other occasions Lisa had met him, she had found him a charming diversion, despite his tendency to become amorous in his boyishly enthusiastic manner. His flattering attentions at first startled and dismayed Lisa, but when she became aware of Adam observing them at times with sardonic amusement, she surrendered to the devilish desire to encourage Kenneth's behaviour. Why she did this, she could not explain to herself, but it was something she regretted very deeply when she encountered Kenneth in the garden one evening while she was taking her usual after-dinner stroll.

'Are you looking for Mr Vandeleur?' Lisa questioned him as he came across the lawn towards her with that long-legged, swinging stride of his.

'No,' he laughed lightly, taking her arm and falling into step beside her. 'I was hoping to see you, Lisa, and here you are. It's almost as if you were waiting for me.'

Lisa stopped abruptly in her stride and stared curiously up into his lean, clean-shaven face. 'You were hoping to see me?'

'From the first moment I saw you I knew you would look beautiful in the moonlight,' he murmured with an unexpected note of passion in his voice that made her stare at him in speechless surprise. 'Your hair is like silver sheen, and in that white dress you look like a princess who has just stepped out of one of Hans Andersen's fairy tales.'

'Kenneth?' Lisa tried to extricate her hands from his, but failed. 'Are you feeling all right?'

'I feel wonderful,' he laughed again, adding with a hint of sensuality in his voice, 'Now that I've seen you.'

'Kenneth, I don't think——'

'You're the most wonderful girl I've ever met,' he interrupted, his hungry grey eyes devouring her face. 'Every time I see you I feel a little lightheaded.'

Cursing herself for foolishly giving him the impression that she was attracted to him, Lisa said a little sharply, 'I think you should go home and take an aspirin.'

'I don't need an aspirin, Lisa. It's *you* I need. I love you,' he declared hotly, lunging at her clumsily and showering her face with kisses.

'Kenneth, have you gone mad?' she demanded, trying to ward off his hungry, seeking mouth. 'Let me go! At once, do you hear!'

Her voice, sharp with anger, finally penetrated, and Kenneth released her abruptly as well as a little shamefacedly. 'I'm sorry, Lisa.'

Filled with instant remorse and guilt, she shook her head and said gently, 'I'm the one who should be apologising.'

'Lisa——'

'Don't say anything,' she interrupted, touching his arm lightly. 'It's all my fault. I like you, Ken, but I realise now that I've misled you from the start.'

'You mean you don't feel the same way about me as I do about you?'

'We've only known each other for a few days,' she evaded having to speak the truth.

Lean-fingered hands gripped hers painfully. 'Do you

mean there's hope for me yet?'

'No,' she whispered, lowering her eyes. 'I'm sorry.'

'How about friendship, then?' Kenneth persisted. 'Are we still friends?'

Lisa's smile was tinged with sadness. 'Friendship is just about all I can offer you.'

'Shall we seal our friendship with a kiss?' Kenneth asked eagerly, and before Lisa could refuse, his soft lips had brushed against hers. 'Goodnight, Lisa.'

Lisa watched him walk quickly across the lawn to where he had parked his small white MG and, as the car roared down the drive, Lisa sighed heavily. She had been a fool to allow matters to go this far, but Adam's attitude had, for some curious reason, acted as a spur, and she had been indiscreet enough to permit Kenneth to flirt with her outrageously. There was perhaps another reason for her behaviour, she finally admitted to herself with some reluctance. Kenneth's flattering attentions had given her sagging morale a boost, and it had done wonders as far as restoring her confidence in herself as a woman.

'That was very touching, I must say, but not very satisfying.'

'What——!' Lisa swung round sharply, her eyes searching the shadows beneath the trees a little wildly before they fastened on to Adam's large frame leaning casually against the gnarled stem of the old oak tree. Her heart skipped an uncomfortable beat as she demanded a little weakly, 'How long have you been standing there?'

'Long enough,' came the abrupt reply.

Lisa drew a careful breath, 'You mean you—you heard?'

'I heard—and saw—everything.'

'That was despicable of you!'

'Perhaps,' Adam agreed, coming out of the shadows with Rolf at his heels, and, as her frightened glance took in his black pants and sweater, she realised why he had managed to make himself so inconspicuous. 'I've watched you leading Rudman on whenever he came to Fairview,' that deep, thundering voice of his berated her, 'and I was fortunate enough to witness the results.'

Embarrassment and anger stung her cheeks. 'I—I hope you found it equally amusing?'

'I did.' There was something in his quiet admission that frightened her, and she turned from him, bent on escape, but a heavy hand came down on to her shoulder, gripping it so firmly that she feared it would be dislocated if she struggled for release. 'Where are you going?'

'I—I'm going inside.'

'No, you're not.' With both her shoulders now in the powerful grip of those large hands, she was swung round to face him, and what she saw in that dark face sent a shiver of apprehension up her spine as he growled, 'There should be a more satisfactory ending to this evening for you.'

A throbbing silence followed his remark, and then she whispered hoarsely, 'What—what do you mean?'

'I'm not a man for flowery speeches, and to repeat Ken Rudman's fairytale description of you is quite unnecessary, but this time you're going to know what it's like to be kissed by a man with experience instead of a young fledgling blundering into his first amorous adventure.'

'Oh, no!' she gasped as a wave of fear washed over her, and then she was fighting, with every ounce of strength she possessed, against the relentless pressure of his arms, until despair made her beat against his chest with clenched fists. 'Let me go ... *please*!'

'For a little thing, you put up quite a fight, Lisa, but you know it's useless, don't you?' he laughed shortly, catching hold of her wrists and twisting them behind her back where he held them with one hand while the other encircled her face and forced it out into the open. 'Don't you?' he demanded.

Lisa could not answer him. She was too utterly at his mercy, and too aware of the hard, electrifying warmth of his body against her own, but, when his fingers caressingly probed the hollow at the base of her throat where a pulse throbbed achingly, helpless tears filled her wide, frightened eyes.

'Please, Mr Vandeleur, don't do this,' she begged unsteadily.

'It will be painless, I assure you,' he replied mockingly, lowering his head until she could feel his warm breath against her mouth. 'Kissing can be quite an enjoyable pastime when it's done correctly.'

'I don't doubt your expertise, but I don't fancy being the recipient under the circumstances,' she argued, but already a frightening weakness was assailing her limbs as his lips teased the corner of her mouth.

'You said that very prettily,' he laughed softly and dangerously, 'but the time for talking is over.'

His mouth took possession of hers now with a deliberate sensuality that swept aside her fragile resistance with devastating results. Her lips were parted beneath the expertise of his, and, as he continued to kiss her with a new intimacy, she felt the final shred of her resistance being torn from her grasp.

Rory's kisses had once excited her, but Adam's lips sparked off a flame that seared through her body, awakening her to a depth of emotion she had not imagined she possessed. She was drowning in a maelstrom of sensations, and then, as she felt the warm, caressing pressure of his hand through the silk at her breast, she knew the first stirrings of desire.

It was *impossible*, and more than a little frightening, but every nerve in her body had come alive to his touch, and when he finally released her she swayed slightly with the intensity of her emotions.

'I said it would be painless, didn't I?' he taunted her mockingly, and her sanity returned painfully when she realised that, unlike herself, Adam had remained emotionally undisturbed.

'You've had your fun at—at my expense,' she said unevenly, her throat working as she fought for control. 'May I go now?'

'In a moment.' The moon had dipped behind the clouds, shrouding them in a darkness that made her shiver involuntarily as she waited for him to speak, and when he did, she felt the colour come and go in her cheeks. 'I employed Rudman to manage Waverley for me, and not for your own personal amusement. If you want entertainment in future, then I suggest you seek it elsewhere.'

'Entertainment?' she questioned, her chaotic mind not quite ready to understand him fully.

'Yes, entertainment,' he repeated with harsh impatience. 'An affair, if you like.'

Lisa felt the colour drain from her face, and somewhere deep inside of her there was a pain she could find no answer for. 'Is that what you think of me? That I'm desperate enough to start an affair with the first man who might be willing enough?'

'Aren't you?'

'No, I certainly am not!' she choked out the words.

'Do you deny that you encouraged Rudman?' he demanded with a note of savagery in his voice that chilled her even more.

'No, I don't deny it, but——' She stopped abruptly. How could she explain the reason for her behaviour when she did not understand herself what had spurred her on to encourage Ken?

'It wasn't Rudman you wanted in the first place, was it?' Adam placed his own interpretation on her silence, and she stared up at him stupidly as the moon reappeared in the sky to accentuate every line of his harsh features.

'I—I don't know what you mean.'

'It was *me* you wanted,' he stated bluntly, and she recoiled from him as if he had struck her.

'You're insane!' she gasped, the wild beat of her heart drowning out the sound of her voice.

Hands of steel jerked her against him with a violence that robbed her momentarily of her breath, and his dark eyes glittered dangerously as they raked her pale features and settled deliberately on her soft, quivering mouth.

'You may call me what you like,' he said through his teeth, 'but you enjoyed my kisses more than you would care to admit, and I'm willing to bet that if I kissed you now you'd enjoy it just as much, if not more.'

'That's not true!' she argued hoarsely, but her treacherous body was already responding to his touch, and once again a flame was ignited within her, sending a sensuous fire racing through her veins. 'Let me go!' she pleaded frantically, more afraid of herself now than of him. 'Oh, please let me go!'

'Not yet, Lisa,' his voice rasped in her ear, and a thousand little shivers of unwanted delight raced along her receptive bloodstream. 'The finale is yet to come.'

She tried to ward him off, but as her hands encountered the hard wall of his chest, she knew the futility of her puny efforts. He was immovable, like a solid slab of concrete, crushing her softness against him while his lips devoured hers with a ruthless and demanding intensity that left no room for coherent thought. She felt like a leaf caught up in one of those miniature whirlwinds she had seen racing across the dry, dusty veld, and it swept her along until she neither knew nor cared where it was taking her.

An eternity seemed to pass before Adam finally released her, and, surfacing slowly from the storm of passion he had succeeded in arousing in her, she leaned weakly against him, trembling as his hands slid caressingly down to her hips and up again to cup the soft swell of her breasts.

'I've proved my point, haven't I?'

Those words were like a splash of iced water in the face, making her realise with stinging clarity just where she was, and what she was doing. With humiliation burning through her like a slow fire, she jerked herself away from him and sought refuge in the uncontrollable anger that was rising within her.

'The only thing you've proved is that, by making use of your superior strength, you're capable of forcing any woman into submission!'

That harsh mouth, which had created such havoc with her emotions, twisted cynically. 'Was it my superior strength that made you respond so passionately and willingly to my kisses?'

Lisa wished the earth would cave in beneath her, but nothing happened. Adam was there, witnessing her humiliation, and enjoying it, no doubt, while she would have given anything at that moment to be able to deny the truth.

'I think you're the most hateful man I've ever met, and if it were not for the twins——'

'If it were not for the twins, I wouldn't tolerate you in my home,' he interrupted coldly. 'Remember that.'

Lisa flinched inwardly. No one could have put her more firmly in her place, and with such cruel precision that she was left in no doubt as to what he thought of her. Adam despised her, but, as she stared desolately after his tall, retreating figure with Rolf close at heel, she knew that she had only herself to blame.

The weather changed towards the end of November, and the heat became unbearable. The veld lay shimmering and parched beneath the merciless rays of the sun, and Lisa felt herself wilting like the vegetation. 'Hot and dusty,' she recalled her disparaging reply to her aunt's remarks, but there was also a certain beauty about the Karoo at this time of the year, Erica Vandeleur informed Lisa during a trip into town one morning with the twins in order to buy their school uniforms.

'After the first good rains,' Mrs Vandeleur explained, 'the veld comes alive with an amazing and colourful variety of wild flowers, and if you're not careful, you'll find yourself becoming enchanted with this part of the country just as I did so many years ago.'

Lisa could not argue with her, for already the Karoo had her in its clutches and, hot and dusty as it might have been at that moment, she was beginning to dread returning to the city. Nowhere could the sunsets be more spectacular, nor the stars more brilliant at night, and if, in a moment of weakness, she were asked to choose, she would choose to remain where the dew lay heavy on the earth in the early morning while the sweet, pungent smell of the Karoo bush permeated the air. Mrs Vandeleur was right, she decided wryly. She would have to take care, or the enchantment of the Karoo would make the parting so much more painful, and having to part from the children was something she did not even want to contemplate as yet.

Her thoughts were cut short as Beaufort West lay before them, and the shopping expedition eventually turned out to be far less laborious than she had imagined it would be. She had driven to town quite often during her stay at

Fairview, and she had mostly taken the children with her in her little Fiat. After browsing through the shops in a leisurely fashion in search of the things she required, she usually treated the twins to an ice-cream in a tea-room, but shopping with Erica Vandeleur was quite a different matter. She knew exactly where to go, and, judging by the treatment they received, Adam and his mother were well-known, respected, and obviously of some importance in the town and district. A little overcome with awe, Lisa moved into the background, but there was no delay in purchasing what they required, and before the twins could become fidgety with boredom, they were on their way back to Fairview with the trunk of Adam's grey Mercedes loaded with parcels.

'Gosh, I can't wait to go to school!' Josh declared excitedly when they finally reached the homestead and were opening up the parcels containing their new clothes and school uniforms, but Kate remained a little apprehensive.

'I wish we didn't have to go to boarding school,' she said, her lips quivering slightly.

'You'll soon get used to it, and you'll enjoy it,' Lisa assured her as she lowered herself on to the bed and drew Kate close against her. 'You'll have so many new friends to play with, and then there's always the weekends to look forward to when you'll be allowed to come home.'

'Will you fetch us in your car, Lisa?'

'No, Josh,' Lisa smiled at him, but her smile was tinged with sadness. 'I shan't be here any more, remember?'

'Why not?' Kate demanded, her eyes as wide and questioning as her brother's, and Lisa swallowed down the lump that rose in her throat.

'I shan't be here because I shall be going back to Cape Town when you start school.'

'But we'll miss you,' they chorused anxiously, and Lisa's

heart swelled with love for them as she hugged them close in an attempt to hide the film of tears in her eyes.

'I'll miss you too,' she admitted, kissing them tenderly on the cheeks.

There was a knock at the door and Lisa looked up to see Daisy entering the children's room.

'Master Adam sent me to tell you that there's a gentleman to see you, Miss Lisa.'

Lisa frowned. 'A gentleman to see me, Daisy?'

'Yes, Miss Lisa.'

'I'll be down in a minute,' Lisa dismissed her after a thoughtful pause, and as the door closed behind Daisy's plump, neatly clad figure, she issued a warning to the twins. 'Don't get up to any mischief while I'm away. I won't be long.'

After a hasty check on her appearance, Lisa went downstairs. Who would want to see her? And why? There was a nervous flutter at the pit of her stomach as she paused on the threshold of the living-room, but, as she recognised the fair, lean young man standing with his back to the door while he spoke to Adam, she drew her breath in sharply and felt the blood drain from her face.

'Rory!'

CHAPTER SEVEN

LISA was hardly aware that she had spoken as she ventured a few paces further into the room, but as Rory Phillips swung round to face her, her eyes involuntarily sought Adam's to find his expression curiously shuttered.

'Lisa *darling*!'

Rory seemed to leap at her from across the room and, before she could prevent it, he had swung her up in his arms and was kissing her hard and passionately on the mouth.

Adam had gone when she finally managed to extricate herself from Rory's arms and, when she stared at the door he had closed so silently behind him, Lisa felt sick with embarrassment, and something else she could not define.

'Was it necessary for you to behave like that in front of Mr Vandeleur?' she berated Rory coldly.

'Oh, come now, Lisa,' he laughed off her remark, his grey eyes moving appreciatively from her corn-coloured hair, which was now long enough to be coiled loosely into her neck, down to her slender, sandalled feet. 'It's not like you to be so standoffish, my darling.'

Lisa suppressed her rising irritation. 'Who told you I was working here?'

'I met your mother in town a few days ago and she gave me your address,' he explained, and then a rueful expression flashed across his lean, handsome face. 'Lisa, I've been an absolute cad to you.'

She stiffened. 'What happened is best kept in the past,

Rory, and there's no need for you to feel bad about anything.'

'You have forgiven me, then?' he demanded eagerly.

'Of course.'

That engaging smile she remembered so well lit up his face, but it no longer had the power to stir her. 'My darling, I can't tell you how relieved I am to hear you say you've forgiven me.'

Lisa was instantly on her guard, and she knew the reason for this when she saw his hand dip into his jacket pocket to emerge a second later with a small velvet-lined box between his fingers. 'Rory——'

'I have your ring here, Lisa. It should never have come off your finger in the first place. Give me your hand.'

Lisa stepped back hastily with a feeling of distaste. 'No, Rory.'

'Lisa?'

There was uncertainty and an almost childlike confusion on every line of his features and, as Lisa stared up at him, she wondered how she could ever have imagined herself in love with him. He was handsome, she had to admit, but he had always been arrogantly aware of the fact that his appearance would get him what he wanted, and now, faced with her refusal, he obviously found it impossible to accept that his looks would not work the same old magic.

'I'm sorry, Rory,' she said with absolute conviction, 'but I don't want to become engaged to you again.'

'I know I treated you badly, Lisa, but don't be so hard on me,' he said persuasively, his confidence returning with remarkable swiftness.

'I apologise if you think I'm being hard on you, but I don't want to wear your ring again,' she persisted, trying a little unobtrusively to increase the distance between them, but Rory followed her laughingly.

'Come now, Lisa, you know you love me.'

'I know nothing of the kind!' she flared hotly, the scar on her face becoming livid.

'Don't deny it, my sweet,' he continued, calmly removing a chair she had placed between them. 'You love me, but I presume you feel you have to punish me in some way.'

'I'm not trying to punish you at all,' she argued, but her statement ended in a gasp as Rory, with unexpected speed, strode across the space dividing them and caught her in his arms. 'Let me go, Rory!' she insisted furiously.

'I'll prove to you that you still love me,' he murmured thickly, and she saw his eyes, dark with a remembered passion, before he lowered his head and sought her lips with his.

Lisa fought against him wildly, twisting her head from side to side to escape his mouth, but his hot, passionate lips found her slender throat, and a shudder of revulsion shook through her. If she had harboured any doubts as to her feelings for this man, then she certainly had none now. Her love for Rory was dead; so dead, it might never even have existed.

'Let me go!' she cried, and, summoning every ounce of strength she possessed, she thrust him from her with a look of disgust on her face.

'Lisa ...' he began incredulously, staggering slightly and breathing heavily as he stood facing her. 'I don't know you like this.'

Lisa controlled the shudders that raced through her with difficulty. 'I don't want your kisses, Rory.'

'My God, there was a time when you couldn't get enough of them!' he exploded, taking out his handkerchief and wiping the perspiration from his forehead and upper lip.

'Yes, I know,' she admitted, lowering her glance ashamedly. 'But that was before the accident.'

'Darling——'

'Please, Rory,' she interrupted hastily. 'I don't want to hurt you unnecessarily, but I don't love you, and I know now that I never really loved you.'

'How can you say that!'

'It's the truth, Rory.' She gestured expressively with her hands. 'Our marriage would have been a mistake; a dreadful mistake.'

'How can you be so sure of that?'

'I *am* sure, Rory. Believe me, I *am*.'

His eyes narrowed speculatively. 'Is there someone else?'

She shook her head. 'There's no one.'

'This Vandeleur chap,' he began suddenly. 'You haven't fallen for him, have you?'

'Don't be ridiculous!' she gasped indignantly, ignoring the odd behaviour of her heart at his suggestion. 'Mr Vandeleur is my employer, and nothing more.'

'Are you certain of that?' he persisted a little cynically. 'It wouldn't be the first time a girl fell in love with her boss, you know?'

'Rory ...' For some obscure reason she could not look him in the eyes just then. 'Please just accept the fact that I don't love you any more. I'm sorry you had to come all this way for nothing, but a telephone call would have saved you the trouble.'

'I won't accept that you no longer love me,' he bit out the words a little anxiously. 'You're still just a little confused, and your mother explained that you were still having problems with your hip. When you're completely well you'll feel differently, you'll see.'

'I won't feel different, and I don't need time to reconsider, Rory,' she replied cuttingly, angry now that he should be so persistent. 'I had plenty of time to consider my feelings for you during those long weeks in hospital, and while I was convalescing at home.'

He spread out his hands in an appealing gesture. 'But *why*, Lisa?'

She stared at him in detached silence for a moment. She had no desire to rake up the past, but it seemed as though she would have to, or Rory would remain unconvinced, and as she started to speak, she felt again the bitterness and the pain of disillusionment.

'The expression on your face when you came to see me in hospital was enough to make me realise that you never really loved me, Rory. If you'd loved me as much as you'd said you did, then it wouldn't have mattered to you what I looked like. I admit I wasn't exactly a pretty sight then, but underneath it all I was still the same person, only that didn't interest you. I returned your ring to you, and you walked out of my life. Oh, yes ...' the hint of cynicism in her smile prevented him from interrupting her, 'I can accept the fact that shock may have made you react in the way you had, but if it had been only shock, then you would have been back long before today.' Her deep blue eyes flashed with derisive mockery. 'What did my mother tell you, Rory? Did she tell you that my scars were not as repulsive as you imagined they would be?'

A dull red colour stained his cheeks and, probably for the first time in his life, he looked embarrassed and uncomfortable, but he had the grace not to deny her allegations. 'I'm only human, Lisa, and I have my faults.'

'I'm only human too, Rory, and I, too, have my faults, but if I've discovered anything about myself over these past months, then it's the certainty that I never loved you. What I felt for you was infatuation. I found you attractive, and you were fun to be with, but marriage is a lifetime of living together, and it demands more than just a superficial attraction to survive.'

'Are you certain you haven't fallen in love with someone else?'

'No, I haven't,' she shook her head adamantly, 'but when I do, it won't be because of the man's outward appearance. It's what's inside that matters most.'

'Lisa——'

'Go back to Cape Town, Rory,' she interrupted tiredly, turning away from him to stare out into the garden and beyond, to where the sheep flocked together beneath a thorn tree in search of protection from the stinging rays of the midday sun. 'Find someone else to wear your ring, and ... be happy, Rory.'

'Do you really mean that?'

'I really mean it,' she said quietly, turning to face him again, and something in her calm, unwavering glance must have finally convinced him that his pleas were fruitless.

'Then I suppose there's nothing else to do except to wish you happiness as well,' he said at last with quiet acceptance, taking her hand in his and looking down at it a little forlornly. 'Goodbye, Lisa.'

He hesitated briefly, almost as if he still hoped she might change her mind, and then he was striding from the room and out of the house to where he had parked his car in the driveway.

Lisa sought refuge from the heat in a cool, refreshing swim after lunch while the children were resting. The weather was too oppressive for her to remain indoors, and Rory's visit that morning had upset her more than she had imagined at first. He had made her aware again of the way she limped, and of the scars which had gradually ceased to matter in the company of people like Adam Vandeleur and his mother. As long as she lived she would never be able to forget the look in Rory's eyes that day he had come to see her in hospital, and the bitterness welled up inside her again to gnaw away at her soul.

In an effort to rid herself of her thoughts she swam several lengths energetically before she simply floated on her back with her eyes closed against the sun. She stayed like that for quite some time, forcing herself to think of nothing but the coolness of the water, and the cicadas shrilling loudly in the heat of the day.

'If only it would rain!' she thought, recalling suddenly a conversation between Adam and Ken Rudman when they had discussed the crippling effect which another season of drought could have on many of the farmers in the district. She had never given the matter much thought before, but when she heard Adam expressing his concern for those less fortunate than he, she listened with quiet interest. The numerous windmills she had seen on the farm provided the soil with subterranean water, making irrigation possible in this area where the rainfall was generally low, but ignorance and insufficient planning often resulted in severe losses. Water was a vital necessity, Lisa discovered, and she felt ashamed to think of the needless waste she had often witnessed in the city.

Birds fluttered from their perch on the overhanging branches of the willow tree, interrupting the flow of her thoughts, and then some sixth sense warned her that she was not alone. She opened her eyes slowly, and her heart leapt into her throat when she saw Adam standing on the edge of the pool. His tall, muscular body was clad in swimming briefs, and his skin had been evenly tanned to a deep ochre. He obviously swam often, she realised absently, but it was not his physical appearance that troubled her at that moment; it was something in that narrow-eyed observation that made her turn and strike out frantically towards the opposite side of the pool. When her hands touched the side, however, Adam surfaced beside her, and the violent thudding of her heart almost choked her when one hard arm encircled her waist, preventing her from raising herself out of the water.

'What's the rush?' he demanded close to her ear.

'I've been here long enough already,' she replied, keeping her back turned resolutely towards him while she brushed the wet strands of hair out of her eyes.

'Another few minutes wouldn't matter, surely?'

'The children——'

'Are resting up in their room, as you should have been doing at this moment,' he finished for her sternly.

'I was too restless.'

'You're still restless,' he observed, taking in her futile attempts to escape him. 'Stop fidgeting.'

'I want to get out of the pool,' she gasped, too aware of his nearness and the quickening of her pulse rate.

'What you're actually trying to say is that you want to get away from me,' he mocked her, and he was so close now that she could feel the length of his hard body against her own. 'What are you afraid of?'

'I'm not afraid of anything,' she lied, and to her horror his hand against her waist shifted its position slightly.

'Do you mean to tell me your heart normally beats this fast?'

A tide of colour swept up from her throat into her cheeks, and there was a hint of desperation in her voice when she begged, 'Let me go!'

'I'll release you if you promise to stay where you are so we can talk,' Adam insisted calmly.

'We have nothing to talk about,' Lisa snapped.

'I can think of plenty.' His arm tightened about her, exerting a threatening pressure about her ribs. 'Do I have your promise that you won't try to escape?'

His breath was warm against her cheek, and she was frantic enough to promise him anything at that moment in order to put some distance between them.

'You have my promise,' she whispered huskily, and suddenly she was free; free of his arm, but not entirely free of him. Adam was taking no chances, and he remained close enough to prevent any effort she might make to escape.

'Your boy-friend left in rather a hurry, didn't he?'

His unexpected reference to Rory made her stiffen. 'Rory is *not* my boy-friend!'

'No?' The mockery in his voice was quite audible without her having to look at him. 'According to what he told me, and judging by the way he greeted you, I would say he was that, and much more.'

Lisa turned then, and her eyes clashed angrily with his, but her anger subsided the next instant just as swiftly as it had risen. Adam looked different, somehow, with his dark hair wet and plastered to his broad forehead. Less austere, she decided vaguely, but still infinitely dangerous.

'I don't care what Rory told you, or what you saw,' she said at last. 'You're mistaken about him being my boy-friend.'

Adam's lips twisted cynically. 'Am I?'

'If you must know,' she began, turning away from the intense scrutiny of his eyes, 'Rory Phillips and I were engaged ... once.'

'I see.'

'No, you don't see at all!' she cried desperately at the cynicism in his voice.

'Then explain it to me.'

'It's none of your business.'

'I'm making it my business,' he said abruptly, and his hands were cruelly punishing about her narrow waist as he turned her in the water to face him. 'This engagement of yours—did it end somewhere around the time of your accident?'

His shrewd guess startled her, but she kept her eyes pinned to his broad chest where the short dark hair clung damply to his skin. 'Yes.'

'Was it because of the accident?' he probed relentlessly. 'Yes.'

'You mean he walked out on you at a time when you most probably needed him most?'

'He walked out on me, yes.' She threw back her head then with a gesture of defiance to meet the force of his dark eyes unwaveringly as she added: 'After *I* broke off the engagement.'

'*You* broke off the engagement?' An incredulous expression flashed across his face. 'Why? Were you just tired of him, or did he say something that led you to believe he no longer wanted to marry you?'

'He didn't *have* to say anything!' she cried in a choked voice, twisting herself free of his hands and, resting her arms on the tiled edge of the pool, she buried her face in them as she explained haltingly, 'It—it was all there in his eyes—the horror, the disgust—and the revulsion. So I—I gave him back his ring and told him it was over between us.'

'I see.' That deep, rumbling voice sounded curiously different without the usual trace of mockery as he continued to question her. 'What made him come all this way specially to see you today?'

Adam had no right to probe into her private affairs in this manner, but she nevertheless heard herself reply with unaccustomed cynicism, 'Apparently he met my mother in town a few days ago, and I can only presume that he discovered I'm not as gruesome-looking as he'd imagined I would be, so he—he had some crazy idea of picking up where we left off with our engagement.'

'And?'

'And nothing,' she snapped, raising her head and glancing at him defiantly over her shoulder.

'You sent him away?'

'I told him it would be best if he returned to Cape Town and forgot about me.'

That hard mouth tightened fractionally. 'Do you find it so difficult to forgive?'

'It's not a question of forgiving. I've forgiven him long ago, but ...' She faltered, lowering her gaze once more to his tanned, muscular chest. 'Our marriage would have been a mistake. I know it now.'

'How can you be so certain of that?'

There had been no difficulty in explaining to Rory, but Adam was an entirely different proposition. What would he know, or understand, about affairs of the heart, when he himself had remained immune to it for thirty-eight years?

'I don't suppose one can be sure of anything in this life,' she managed eventually, 'but I only know that there's no future for me with Rory.'

'With whom does your future lie, then?'

Her pulses leapt nervously. 'With—with no one.'

'Oh, come now,' he scoffed ruthlessly. 'You're an attractive girl with plenty to offer a man, and you shouldn't let a few scars and a slight limp stand in your way.'

He had touched a sore point with a cruel finger, and she winced inwardly. 'Most men look for perfection, and I'm— I'm no longer as perfect as I would like to be.'

Adam's eyes hardened. 'So you're going to crawl into that little shell of yours and exclude men from your life?'

'If you like to put it that way ... yes.'

Strong white teeth flashed in a smile of derision. 'Be careful self-pity doesn't turn you into a sour old spinster.'

'How dare you!' she gasped, her blue eyes sparkling with anger. 'I don't pity myself!'

'Don't you?' His eyes narrowed dangerously. 'You're giving a pretty good demonstration of feeling sorry for yourself.'

Lisa's hand was itching to slap that smug look off his face, but she knew instinctively that she would be made to suffer for it afterwards. 'I wish you'd leave me alone! Your opinions are of no interest to me.'

'Where are you going?' he demanded, following her out of the pool to where she had left her things.

'Back to the house,' she snapped without turning.

'To crawl into your shell where you can lick your wounds in private?'

His stinging remark made her swing round abruptly to face him, and her eyes blazed with helpless fury up into his. 'You're insufferable! You're——'

'Calm down, Lisa.' His hands gripped her shoulders, sending a charge of electricity through her that merely infuriated her more as he said through his teeth, 'God knows, I can do without the company of a spitfire this afternoon.'

'If you'll let go of me, then I'll relieve you of my company, Mr Vandeleur,' she retorted coldly.

'You may be a little spitfire at times, Lisa, but I'm also well aware of your blessed calmness and serenity.' Her startled glance seemed to amuse him, but his eyes lacked their usual lustre, and she was now curiously aware of the signs of tiredness about his mouth and eyes. 'I need your serenity this afternoon,' he added simply.

Anger made way for an instant rush of compassion, and she relaxed in his hold, allowing him to draw her down unresistingly on to the soft grass at their feet.

They did not speak as they lay on their backs, soaking up the sun, and listening to the birds fluttering and fighting loudly in the trees around them. There was, for the first time, a strange new affinity between them, but Lisa dared not probe too deeply for a suitable explanation. It was bewildering enough to know that he needed her at that moment, even though he so obviously despised her.

Adam stirred beside her eventually, and she opened her eyes nervously to find that he had raised himself up on to one elbow to lie staring down at her. His eyes, dark and piercing, held hers effortlessly for several suffocating seconds before he raised his hand to lightly caress the raised, faintly livid scar on her face. An odd little pulse quivered in her throat at his touch, and then she was suddenly too afraid to move.

'You don't need Ken Rudman's flattery and boyish innuendoes to convince you that you're still infinitely desirable,' he said unexpectedly, and at her swift indrawn breath he smiled faintly. 'That's the reason you encouraged him, isn't it?'

Too surprised to think up a clever reply, she stammered, 'Yes, I—I suppose so.'

'I knew it,' he muttered softly with a self-satisfied expression on his face, and she squirmed inwardly with remembered humiliation.

'If you knew, then why——?' The words stuck in her throat. It was impossible to speak of those moments in his arms, and she questioned instead his accusations. 'You—you didn't really think I was hankering after an affair, did you?'

'No.' He sat up abruptly to stare out across the pool, and she had the absurd desire to slide her hand across his broad back to feel the muscles rippling beneath her fingertips, but she checked herself forcibly when he spoke. 'I said a lot of things that night to hurt you, but I was angry with you for having so little faith in yourself as a woman.'

'Why should my lack of faith in myself trouble you?' she asked incredulously.

'Heaven only knows, but it does.' He turned then, and she was suddenly intensely conscious of the fact that her swimsuit accentuated every line and curve of her slim body for his bold and quite deliberate inspection, but there was also a disturbing hint of devilment in the eyes that observed her so closely. 'Perhaps it's because you're such a little thing that I feel the need to protect you, even from yourself.'

'I can look after myself.'

She sat up agitatedly as she spoke, her fingers groping for the sleeveless towelling robe, but Adam leaned over her suddenly, and a large brown hand gripped her wrist, halting her action and sending a spark of awareness tingling along her nerves.

'Can you?' he demanded in a dangerous undertone, and he was now so close that she could see the tiny flecks of gold in his dark brown eyes as they burned deeply into hers. 'Can you look after yourself, Lisa?'

His hand slid up her arm to grip her shoulder even as frantic little plans to escape assumed formation in her mind, and then it was too late. He was bending over her, forcing her back on to the soft grass, and the width of his shoulders blotted out the sun as his lips brushed across her eyelids, forcing her lashes down over her wide, frightened eyes before he took possession of her tremulous mouth.

Lisa knew the futility of fighting against those imprisoning arms, and held herself rigid and unresponsive, but the gentle, persistent pressure of his mouth finally broke through her barrier of reserve and parted her lips. She experienced again that wild, leaping response within her, and then nothing seemed to matter beyond the fact that Adam was kissing her with a hungry, almost tender passion, so different from the way he had kissed her before.

When his mouth finally left hers, it was to explore her slender throat, and the smoothness of her creamy shoulder where his impatient fingers had paved the way by brushing aside the narrow strap of her swimsuit. His lips against her skin sent the blood pounding like molten fire through her veins, but the persistence of a warning little voice made her cling desperately to the final shred of her sanity.

'Adam.' Her voice sounded strangled and quite unlike her own. 'I—I must get back to the children.'

'Later,' he muttered against her throat.

'Adam ... this is madness!' she gasped, but he was deaf to her pleas as his mouth trailed a blazing path down to the fullness of her breast.

Inhibited as she was, allowing Adam this new and devastating intimacy seemed suddenly so wonderfully right, and, as a sensual warmth flowed into her limbs, she began to know the full meaning of desire and the aching need for fulfilment. She could no longer think coherently, and neither had she the desire to try as her untutored body responded with a will of its own to Adam's tempestuous caresses. Her hands moved of their own volition to become entangled in the thick crispness of his hair, and then a low moan escaped past her lips as she surrendered herself to the wild new ecstasy pulsating through her.

Lisa often wondered afterwards what would have happened had Willa Jackson's 'Hello there!' not shattered the intimacy between Adam and herself at that moment. While sanity returned to her in wave after wave of paralysing shame, Adam seemed to be in complete control of himself, and strangely unperturbed at the thought of Willa witnessing their passionate embrace.

'Good afternoon, Willa,' he said calmly, getting to his feet and drawing Lisa up with him, and then, whether by accident or design, his body shielded Lisa's, giving her that much-needed opportunity to restore some respectable order to her appearance as Adam asked: 'What brings you here at this time of the day?'

Willa stepped across the space dividing them, and Lisa felt a flicker of envy stab her heart. Willa was beautiful, competent, elegant, and faintly seductive even in her usual riding clothes, but there was a glittering hardness in her eyes that did not match the smile on her coral-pink lips as she tilted her head up at Adam.

'Daddy's having problems with the electro-generator and he wondered if you would have time to take a look at it for him this afternoon.'

Adam picked up his towel and draped it carelessly across one broad shoulder and, as he did so, his eyes met Lisa's briefly. It seemed to her, in her chaotic state of mind, that he was about to say something, then he shrugged his shoulders and turned to face Willa.

'Give me a few minutes to get dressed, will you?' he said, pushing his feet into his canvas shoes, and then he was striding towards the house.

'Oh, Miss Moreau,' Willa interrupted Lisa's hasty preparation to take flight, 'keep me company, won't you?'

CHAPTER EIGHT

'KEEP me company,' Willa had said, but one quick glance into those cold green eyes told Lisa that it was not company Willa wanted; it was a confrontation, and Lisa did not need clairvoyancy to guess the subject.

'If you don't mind, Miss Jackson, I must get back to the children.'

'What I have to say won't take more than a few minutes.'

'Very well, then,' Lisa agreed reluctantly and, striving for an outward calmness, she turned to face Willa. 'What is it you have to say to me?'

'I'd like to give you some advice, my dear,' Willa smiled faintly, but her eyes remained cold as they swept disdainfully over Lisa. 'Don't make a fool of yourself over Adam. Like most men he'll take what he can get if the girl is willing enough, but don't place too much significance on his behaviour. He's already committed himself elsewhere.'

There was a soaring sensation in Lisa's ears, and a pounding against her temples that made her sway slightly on her feet. If Willa had struck her physically with that riding crop she kept twisting between her beautiful hands, Lisa could not have felt more stunned. *Adam was committed*, and to Willa, judging by the look of intense satisfaction on those classically carved features, and Lisa felt a coldness surging through the mist of inexplicable pain; a coldness that left her peculiarly without feeling at that moment, and she shivered despite the heat.

'You're making it sound as though Adam's a rake,

committing himself to one woman while still taking advantage of others,' she heard herself speak in a voice that was oddly detached.

'Oh, no! Don't misunderstand me!' Willa corrected her hastily. 'Adam is a very respected man in this community, and he's also a very wealthy man, as you must have guessed. This has been sufficient reason for some women to go a little silly over him, only to be discarded the moment they began to bore him, and I'm telling you all this because I wouldn't want to see you hurt unnecessarily.'

Lisa felt herself go rigid with distaste. 'Are you suggesting that I've thrown myself at him because of his wealth and position in this district?'

Willa smiled sweetly. 'I'm not suggesting that at all, but living under the same roof with him must surely make it difficult to keep your relationship on a businesslike footing all the time, and it's only natural that a certain intimacy might develop between you, only ...' she paused significantly, 'don't take it seriously. To Adam it's merely a flirtation, and you're the one who'll be hurt in the end.'

Lisa was not fooled by Willa's display of concern. This girl was concerned for herself, and for no one else, and Lisa could almost feel sorry for her if what she had said was the truth.

'If Adam has committed himself, as you say, doesn't it trouble you to know about these ... lapses?'

'We're two of a kind, my dear,' Willa smiled, drawing herself up to her full height and looking down at Lisa with a look of triumph on her face as she added with a hint of intimacy in her voice, 'Adam and I understand each other perfectly.'

Lisa stared at her blankly for a moment, not sure whether to congratulate her or to commiserate with her, but she finally decided against both.

'You must excuse me, Miss Jackson,' she said with a calmness and dignity that was beginning to crumble. 'The children will be wondering what's happened to me.'

'You *will* remember what I told you?'

How can I *forget*! Lisa thought in anguish as she nodded silently and followed the path Adam had taken up to the house some minutes ago.

Lisa walked as if her life depended on it. She dared not stop to think, but with each step she took her mind seemed to shout 'Adam and Willa! Adam and Willa!' She had suspected it from the start; she had even considered it a perfect match. Why then should it hurt so much?

'Don't *think*! Don't *feel*! Just *walk*!' she told herself fiercely, but later, in the privacy of her room, her rigid control snapped, and shame and humiliation swept through her with the devastation of a hurricane that tore at her until she felt totally disembodied.

She had surrendered herself to Adam's lovemaking as she had never done with any other man before, but for him it had been only a brief interlude, while to her . . . !

She could still feel the touch of his lips and hands on her body and, shuddering violently, she sagged on to the bed and buried her quivering face in her hands. How he must be laughing now at the easy victory he had scored over her, and how he must despise her for her weakness once again! She had been taken in by his apparent understanding; by his surprising and seemingly genuine concern for her; and finally by his sheer masculinity, but he had merely been playing with her. He had led her on deliberately until she had made a humiliating spectacle of herself. She had credited him with sincerity, and he had shattered her trust.

'Adam and Willa! Adam and Willa!'

Their names went well together, she thought dully,

lowering her hands to stare at the carpet with unseeing eyes.
Willa would, of course, be the perfect wife for him. She
could see that now, but ...! Oh, *God*! Why did it hurt so
much? Why, why, *why*!

The answer came with a shattering force that made her
reel mentally beneath the impact, but she fought against it;
denied it passionately; and finally was forced to succumb
to the inexorable truth. She was in love with Adam. It was
ludicrous, impossible, and forbidden! She should hate him
for what he had done to her, but she loved him instead.
There was no joy in this knowledge, and no delirious up-
surge of excitement. There was only that blinding pain
which was worse than anything she had ever known before. Adam belonged to Willa and—pray God—she would
be gone before their marriage.

A shout of childish laughter from the room next to hers
made Lisa start nervously, and a quick glance at the time
sent her hurrying into the bathroom to shower and change
into a cool, cotton frock. She dried her hair vigorously
with a towel, brushing it thoroughly before she twisted it
into a knot at her neck, and applied a touch of make-up to
her face. She was pale beneath her newly acquired tan, but,
with luck, no one would notice, and with Adam away working on Howard Jackson's electro-generator, Lisa had the
rest of the afternoon in which to find the courage to face
him again.

An absorbing game of marbles with the twins temporarily
took her mind off things, but, when the game came to an
end, Lisa sank into a fit of depression from which there
seemed to be no escape. Josh and Kate were fortunately
too involved with diverting the path of a hairy worm to
notice any change in Lisa, but Erica Vandeleur's shrewd
glance missed nothing when she called Lisa to join her on
the verandah for a long, cool orange drink.

'You're looking rather pale, child,' she remarked with concern as the silence lengthened between them. 'Aren't you feeling well?'

'It's this heat,' Lisa explained, and it was not altogether a lie, for her body felt clammy and uncomfortable with perspiration despite her recent shower.

'Yes, it does sap one's energy at times,' Mrs Vandeleur replied absently, her grey-green eyes searchingly intent upon Lisa. 'You *are* happy here with us, Lisa, aren't you?'

Lisa stared out across the colourful garden, but her glance lingered with tenderness on the tousled-haired twins where they played on the lawn. 'I'm not unhappy here, Mrs Vandeleur.'

'You're not missing the city life?'

'Oh, no,' Lisa said quickly, glancing at the older woman just in time to witness a flicker of humour flash across her lined face.

'Am I right in thinking you'll be sorry to leave here?'

'Yes.'

Lisa looked away. There was too much pain inside her at that moment. There was the pain of loving unwisely, and the pain of knowing she would have to leave eventually, but she would not be able to bear the pain of having to stay and witness Adam marrying Willa Jackson. There was pain, too, at having to leave this slightly barren but beautiful part of the country where the sunsets held you spellbound, and the stars clustered like diamonds in the night sky.

'The Karoo has cast its spell on you,' Erica Vandeleur observed quietly as if she had caught the drift of Lisa's thoughts.

'Yes, I'm afraid it has,' Lisa laughed shortly, but she looked away hastily when her throat tightened and her eyes filled with tears.

The ringing of the telephone saved the situation for her and, as Erica Vandeleur went to answer it, Lisa pulled herself together and dashed away her tears. It was ridiculous and foolish to weep over something which could never be hers, and the sooner she accepted this fact the sooner she would get over it.

'That was Adam,' Erica Vandeleur explained when she came out on to the verandah a few minutes later. 'The Jacksons have invited him to dinner. He's working on their generator, and it may take some time yet to repair it. It's a nuisance really, but they've done so much to help him in the past since Jacques——' Her voice broke slightly, then she sighed resignedly. 'Oh, well, I'd better go and see what's going on in the kitchen ... and you'd better check up on those two little horrors of ours,' she added laughingly as shrieks of excitement reached their ears.

Lisa hurried down into the garden and was just in time to save a chameleon from being submerged in the fish pond.

'Oh, Lisa!' Josh and Kate complained almost simultaneously as she set the creature free. 'We wouldn't have let it drown.'

'Perhaps not,' Lisa agreed, 'but it would have been cruel.'

'Can we go for a swim?' Josh demanded, casting aside the incident with the speed of an energetic child and, as Lisa agreed, he grabbed Kate's hand. 'Let's go and put on our costumes. Quick!'

Lisa did not join the children in the pool on this occasion, but sat quietly on the grass while she kept an eye on them. The memory of what had happened there earlier that afternoon was still too vivid in her mind, and, as her pulse quickened, she concentrated fiercely on the twins while they splashed about in the water. They were both good swimmers for their age, Lisa realised once again as she watched their deeply tanned little bodies moving about lithely in the water, but she agreed with Adam's ruling that the pool was forbidden to them unless they were accompanied by an adult.

A dragonfly hovered above the sparkling water and they shrieked with laughter as their efforts to splash it failed. Lisa smiled indulgently at their antics, but, as their bath-time drew near, she ordered them out and took them back to the house.

'Can't we stay up a bit later this evening?' Josh pleaded when it was eventually time to put out the light.

'No, you can't,' Lisa replied firmly as she tucked them up in bed.

'But Uncle Adam isn't here. You said so,' Josh persisted.

'That makes no difference. Rules are rules, and you're going to sleep right now.'

'Oh, no!'

'Oh, yes!' Lisa insisted.

'Uncle Adam won't know if we stay up just a teeny bit longer,' Josh pouted, adding persuasively, 'and Gran won't mind.'

Lisa straightened between the two beds and looked down at them with as much sternness as she could muster. 'Your uncle gave me very strict instructions, Josh, and I daren't disobey him.'

'But, Lisa ...'

'No, Joshua.'

There was a startled silence, and their usually dirty faces looked almost angelic with cleanliness as they stared up at her in wide-eyed dismay.

'You only call me Joshua when you're angry,' Josh said at last, and the hurt look in his eyes very nearly succeeded in shattering her resolve, but the thought of Adam's anger saved the situation.

'I'm not angry with you, but you must go to sleep now,' she said a little more gently as she picked up a few scattered toys and put them where they belonged.

A whispered conversation took place between the twins, but Lisa pretended not to notice, and when she finally turned to face them, two very serious-looking children were staring up at her from beneath the sheets.

'Lisa,' Kate began hesitantly, 'don't you love us any more?'

Lisa's heart twisted painfully, and she was on her knees between their beds almost instantly, hugging each one of them in turn. 'I love you both to bits,' she explained with a lump in her throat, 'but I can't allow you to stay up later than usual. Your uncle will be very angry with me, and you wouldn't want that, would you?'

'No,' they both agreed solemnly.

'All right, then,' Lisa smiled, smoothing down their dark curls with gentle, loving hands.

'Why doesn't Uncle Adam love us too?'

'But of course he loves you,' Lisa replied instantly to Josh's unexpected question, but he was far from satisfied.

'He never ever plays with us,' he said truthfully, and Kate added: 'He just always scowls at us.'

'Your uncle is a very busy man,' Lisa prevaricated, finding it difficult to argue against the truth, but she had to defend Adam somehow. 'There's so much to do on the farm, and——'

'But he's always riding around with that lady from next door,' Josh interrupted frowningly.

'Well, I——' Lisa faltered and bit her lip. What was there she could say to that? she wondered helplessly.

'Is she going to be our aunty?' Kate asked, and her

anxiety found an echo in Lisa's heart.

'I ... don't know,' she replied carefully. 'Perhaps.'

'I think I'd hate that,' Josh exploded, his thunderous expression bearing an uncanny resemblance to his uncle's.

'Oh, no, you mustn't say that,' Lisa whispered anxiously.

'But it's true,' Josh insisted, 'and you said we must always tell the truth.'

'Yes, but——' Lisa faltered, at a loss for words, then she resolutely tried to bring an end to the conversation. 'It's time I put the light out.'

'*She* doesn't like us either,' Kate's remark stopped her in the act of reaching for the light switch between their beds, and Lisa needed no explanation as to whom Kate was referring to.

'Miss Jackson hasn't had much to do with you, so how can you say that?' Lisa rebuked her gently.

'We just know,' Josh explained a little defiantly.

'Why can't *you* marry Uncle Adam?' Kate wanted to know. 'Then you'll be our aunty.'

Lisa's hands trembled as she straightened the sheets once more. 'I couldn't do that.'

'Why not?' the twins demanded with childish arrogance.

'Because——' Lisa took a steadying breath. 'Because your uncle and I ... we don't feel that way about each other.'

'What way?' Josh frowned.

'Well, we don't—love—each other.'

'But can't you——?'

'No, I can't, and your uncle certainly won't,' Lisa cut in abruptly, rising to her feet as an indication that the conversation had gone far enough. 'Now, shut your eyes and go to sleep so I can put out the light.'

'Aren't you going to kiss us goodnight?' Kate demanded tremulously, and Lisa's heart melted.

'Yes, of course I am,' she smiled warmly as she bent over them and kissed them lightly on their foreheads. 'Goodnight.'

'Goodnight, Lisa,' they chorused, snuggling down beneath the sheets, and Lisa stood looking down at them for a moment with a lump in her throat before she switched off the light and left the room.

The conversation she had had with the twins disturbed Lisa more than she cared to admit even to herself, and her attention wandered on several occasions at the dinner table, resulting in the embarrassing situation of having to ask Erica Vandeleur to repeat herself.

It was a dark night, Lisa noticed when they went out on to the verandah after dinner in search of a breath of fresh air. Clouds had appeared from somewhere to gather swiftly in the sky, and the stars were obliterated from view, but the heat remained oppressive and slightly ominous.

'The weather looks promising, but then one never can tell,' Mrs Vandeleur remarked, and, when Lisa did not reply, she glanced at her sharply. 'You've been very quiet this evening, Lisa. Have the children been particularly trying today?'

'No, not really,' Lisa smiled faintly into the darkness. 'They wanted to stay up later this evening, but I'm afraid I couldn't allow it.'

'No, of course not,' the older woman agreed, and they lapsed into silence once more.

'Mrs Vandeleur ...' Lisa began eventually, the cane chair creaking beneath her weight as she altered her position nervously, 'how does Adam feel about the twins?'

'What do you mean, my dear?'

'I mean ... is he fond of them?'

'Naturally he is, and he's very concerned that they should have the kind of upbringing Jacques would have wished them to have.' She paused briefly and Lisa could feel those eyes searching her face in the darkness. 'Why do you ask?'

'It's something Josh and Kate mentioned when I put them to bed,' Lisa explained, pushing her hair away from her forehead and grimacing when her hand came away damp. 'Adam never takes much notice of them, and they seem to think that he—that he doesn't like them very much.'

'What nonsense!' Mrs Vandeleur exploded. 'I hope you told them they're mistaken?'

'I tried, but——' Lisa passed the tip of her tongue over her dry lips nervously, 'I don't think I convinced them somehow.'

'The guardianship of the twins is a tremendous responsibility, and Adam ...' Erica Vandeleur paused, obviously realising that there was some truth in the children's suppositions, and then, like Lisa, she tried to excuse his behaviour. 'He hasn't much time lately for himself and for his family.'

'I know.'

'Perhaps I should speak to him, but—Oh, dear,' she sighed heavily. 'He's been so boorish lately, and when he's like that, it's best to leave him be.'

'I suppose so,' Lisa agreed with her, but the problem still remained unsolved. The children felt unloved, and Adam was sublimely oblivious of the fact that his callous behaviour was the cause of it.

'What he really needs is a wife,' Erica Vandeleur said at length. 'It's time he settled down with a family of his own.'

'It's time *who* settled down, Mother?' a deep voice enquired out of the shadows, and Lisa's heart leapt into her throat as a dark shape loomed up in front of them.

Adam had approached the house so quietly that neither

of them had heard him, and, as he leaned back against the wooden rails surrounding the verandah, Lisa could almost sense a certain anger vibrating through him as he crossed his arms over his chest.

'Good heavens, Adam! You startled me,' his mother exclaimed, but Adam had no intention of being diverted.

'Whose life are you trying to organise this time, Mother?'

'Yours, Adam,' came the undaunted reply, and Lisa could not help but admire her fearlessness. 'It's time you found yourself a wife. Someone gentle, loving, and warm-hearted enough to smooth off the rough edges, and someone who would mellow you slightly.'

'That sounds delightful,' Adam mocked his mother. 'Have you someone like that in mind?'

'No, but——' Erica Vandeleur paused, and then said quite distinctly, 'It will have to be someone like Lisa, I think.'

Lisa felt as if she had been flung into a bath of ice cubes, and then, painfully, the blood surged back into her body while she wished frantically that she could shrink quietly into oblivion.

'Why someone *like* Lisa?' Adam was demanding in that harsh, mocking voice of his. 'Why not suggest Lisa herself?'

'Nothing would please me more,' his mother stated adamantly and, having set the cat among the pigeons, she rose to her feet. 'Now, if you'll excuse me, I'm going to have an early night.'

Lisa had no intention of remaining out there alone with Adam, and she hastily followed Mrs Vandeleur, muttering apologetically, 'I have a few letters to write.'

'Just a minute.' No matter how much she had wanted to escape, the imperious command in that thundering voice could not be ignored, and Lisa turned back slowly to face the man she feared ... yet loved above all else.

'Was there something you wanted to discuss with me?' she asked in a voice that sounded deceptively calm.

Adam pushed himself away from the rails and moved a little into the light emitted from the living-room window, but the sardonic amusement etched so clearly on his features made her wish he had remained in the shadows.

'What do you think of my mother's suggestion?' he demanded suddenly, and Lisa felt the tension spiral through her body.

'I would prefer not to think about it at all.'

'I don't appeal to you as a husband, then?'

'I didn't come to Fairview to look for a husband, and your mother was merely speculating,' she side-stepped the question. 'She would like to see you married and—and settled, that's all—but not necessarily with me.'

'Who would *you* suggest, then, as a suitable wife for me?'

Lisa looked away from those eyes that saw so much of what she hoped to hide, and her voice was coldly detached as she said: 'I wouldn't presume to make any suggestions.'

'A pity,' he murmured mockingly. 'It might have been interesting to hear your views on the subject.' His hand came down on her shoulder unexpectedly. 'About this afternoon.'

Lisa flinched away from his touch as if she had come into contact with a red-hot branding iron. 'If you don't mind, Mr Vandeleur, I would rather not discuss it.'

Adam pushed his hands into the pockets of his pants and smiled a little cynically. 'I thought we'd progressed beyond the "Mr Vandeleur" stage.'

Lisa's colour rose sharply at the thought of the intimacy they had shared, and she silently blessed the darkness for its protection as she said tritely, 'I don't want to talk about it!'

'All right, we won't talk about it,' Adam snapped, his voice harsh with impatience. 'Let's just forget the entire incident, if that will make you happy, but will you explain to me, please, why you felt it necessary to run like a scared rabbit the moment my mother went into the house?'

'I didn't run, I——'

'Oh, yes, you did,' he interrupted forcefully, 'and you've been poised for flight from the moment we were left alone.'

'I haven't! I was——' His hand was at her throat, momentarily making her lose her voice as he forced her back against the rails, then the pressure of his fingers relaxed and moved in a slow, caressing motion round to the nape of her neck. 'Don't do that!' she gasped in a strangled voice.

'What are you afraid of Lisa? Me? Or yourself?'

'I don't know what you're talking about,' she said icily, at a disadvantage now with the living-room light playing across her taut features. 'I'm not afraid of anyone ... or anything.'

'I think you are, and I also think I know what it is.'

The sensuality flowing from his fingers was beginning to penetrate the barrier of cool detachment she had erected about herself, and she said sharply, 'Don't touch me!'

Adam removed his hand, but he brought it down on to the rail beside her to imprison her securely without actually touching her. 'When you were engaged to Rory, didn't he occasionally make love to you a little?'

'Certainly not!' she cried indignantly.

'I thought so,' Adam smiled faintly as he observed her heightened colour. 'There's a certain innocence about you, Lisa, that made me suspect that Rory what's-his-name was never permitted the intimacies you allowed me this afternoon, and that's what's troubling you, isn't it?'

'Oh, please,' she groaned, her cheeks burning with the

fire of her shame and humiliation. 'We agreed we wouldn't discuss it.'

'So we did,' he murmured thoughtfully, 'but you intrigue me, Lisa. You're a disturbing little creature at the best of times, and your eyes contain secrets that incite my curiosity. Your mouth suggests a hidden passion not yet explored, and it makes me wonder ...' He paused significantly, and her senses were suddenly alert to the aura of sensuality that clung to him. 'It makes me wonder what you'll be like when you're totally aroused,' he concluded his tantalising statement softly.

'You—you have no right to—to talk to me like this,' she rebuked him unsteadily, her body tingling as if he had actually touched her.

'No, I haven't the right, have I,' he agreed, so close to her now that she could almost feel the heat of his body against her own. 'I must admit, though, that the temptation is very strong to continue where we left off this afternoon.'

'Oh, no! Please!' she begged in alarm, her heart beating so fast that it felt as though it would leap out of her throat.

'Stop your trembling, Lisa,' he instructed harshly. 'I have no desire to force my unwanted attentions on you. Go up to your room and write your letters like a good little girl, if that's what you want, and ...' He moved away from her then, and added: 'Pleasant dreams.'

CHAPTER NINE

IN the seclusion and safety of her room Lisa paused to take stock of herself, and she was surprised to discover that Adam had been right. She *was* trembling, and she had trembled so much down there on the verandah that, for one terrifying moment, she had been afraid that she might collapse at his feet, but, with her head held high, she had forced her unwilling limbs into action and had walked away from him. She had moved awkwardly, aware of his eyes following her limping progress, and she had been close to tears when she finally crossed the spacious hall and climbed the stairs up to her room.

'Pleasant dreams,' Adam had wished her, but her dreams were anything *but* pleasant that night. The nightmares she had suffered after the accident returned, and Adam stepped into them with the stealthiness of a panther to stalk her ruthlessly and menacingly. She fled from him as if he were the devil himself, but her movements were slow and retarded. Her breath was rasping in her throat with the effort to escape those grasping hands, but she was captured just as the sky was rent with a terrifying flash of fire. She screamed and fought like a wild thing, but his hands were bruising her shoulders as he held her down.

'Lisa!' his voice shattered her semi-conscious state, and her dream had suddenly become reality.

Adam was bending over her, his harsh features acquiring terrifying proportions in the dull light of the bedside lamp as he shook her and called her name again. The sky and the earth seemed to come together in a blinding flash and a frightening crash of thunder, and his hand against her mouth stifled the involuntary scream that rose from her raw, aching throat.

She went limp with fear in his grasp, her eyes wide and almost purple as she stared up into that ruggedly chiselled face. There was a violent storm raging outside, she realised at last, but the horror of her nightmare was still upon her as Adam removed his hand from her mouth, and the quick rise and fall of her breasts beneath the frothy lace still conveyed her agitation.

'What—what are you—you doing in m-my bedroom?' she whispered hoarsely, her fingers against her aching throat as she continued to stare up at him with fear still lurking in her eyes, but subconsciously she assimilated the fact that it must be somewhere close to midnight, and that Adam was still fully clothed.

'I was checking the windows down this end of the passage when I heard you scream,' he explained quietly, pouring water into a glass and seating himself on the side of the bed as she sat up to take it from him thankfully, but her hands shook so much that he had to hold the glass for her while she drank thirstily. 'Was it the storm, or a nightmare?' he wanted to know when she indicated that she had had enough.

'I don't ... know,' she lied unsteadily.

'A little bit of both, perhaps?' he suggested, his eyes flicking over her with interest, and making her aware suddenly of the transparency of her nightgown.

With her cheeks flaming, she jerked the sheets up to beneath her chin, and the storm outside seemed to be raging within her as well. The rain lashed against the window mercilessly, and she flinched inwardly as a flash of lightning tore across the sky with earth shattering results, but the storm was no longer only outside; it was in the room all around her, and the air seemed to be crackling with electricity.

'I'm all right now,' she croaked jerkily, desperate now that he should leave her alone.

'Are you sure?'

'Yes ... thank you.'

His keen glance took in the whiteness of her thin cheeks, the disarray of her corn-gold hair, and the eyes dark and wide with some inner stress, but it was on the soft, quivering mouth that she fought so valiantly to control that his glance lingered.

'My God, you're *not* all right,' he said thickly, and then she was gathered into his arms.

He held her firmly but gently, cradling her against him as if she were a child in need of comfort and, suddenly, she was just that. Tremors shook through her with a terrible force in the aftermath of her nightmare, and then, as the well-remembered tension uncoiled very slowly within her, she sagged against him weakly. Emotionally drained and spent, she buried her face against him and was perfectly still.

How long he sat like that with her she could not recall, but she was quite content to remain where she was when she eventually felt his lips moving against her temple, her warm cheek, and finally her faintly feverish lips.

To resist never occurred to her at that moment, but his lips lingered, and the kiss deepened until a fire was kindled inside her. His hands were no longer merely comforting her, but caressing her until their warmth through the thinness of her nightgown made her skin tingle in response. Everything receded into the background; the storm, her nightmares, and also Willa's warnings. The only thing that made any sense at all at that moment was the sanctuary of his strong arms about her, and the heaven of his lips on hers, but heaven, too, had to end somewhere, she discovered when his arms fell away from her pulsating, responsive body.

Confused and bewildered, she stared up into his dark, unfathomable eyes, and then his lips curved into that cynical smile she was beginning to know so well.

'I didn't intend to do that, but I don't regret it either,' he said harshly, and reality was thrust upon her rudely, and shatteringly.

She had needed comfort, and he had given it. What happened afterwards she had only herself to blame for. She had offered her lips willingly, and Adam had reacted accordingly.

'I—I think you'd better go,' she whispered unsteadily, veiling her pain-filled eyes with her lashes.

'I think so too, or I might be tempted to take an encore,' he agreed mockingly, getting to his feet and drawing himself up to his full height. 'Goodnight again, Lisa.'

She stared at the door for a long time after he had closed it softly behind him. He had used the word 'tempted'. 'I might be tempted to take an encore.'

Had she really tempted him?

A quivering sigh escaped her as she leaned back against the pillows and switched off the light. The violence of the storm had passed, but the rain continued to beat against the window panes. Lisa watched it running down in rivulets against the glass, and, as she sighed again, the words of a half-forgotten poem struggled to the surface of her mind.

> Alas, how easily things go wrong!
> A sigh too much, or a kiss too long,
> And there follows a mist and a weeping rain,
> And life is never the same again.

The rest of it was tantalisingly vague, but it could almost

have been written entirely for her. She had sighed too much, and kissed too long, and life would never be the same again.

'Love, true and enduring, is a once-in-a-lifetime emotion, and the rest are but poor substitutes,' her Aunt Molly had once told her. 'That's why marriage to someone else is unthinkable. No one could ever compare with Luke, no matter how hard they tried, and we would have ended up making each other's lives a misery.'

Aunt Molly had been right, Lisa thought unhappily. Her love for Adam was that 'once-in-a-lifetime' thing for her, and no one could ever hope to compare favourably with him.

The storm had lasted all night, washing away fences and uprooting trees which had stood in the path of the deluge. Lightning had struck the grass roof of a labourer's hut, setting it alight, but fortunately no one had been hurt, and for two days afterwards Adam and his men worked almost round the clock to repair the damage.

Teamwork was of the utmost importance if Adam did not want to lose more of his livestock than he already had done, and Lisa found herself lending a voluntary hand in the kitchen to prepare food and drink for the men as they came in in relays. It was her first taste of what life on a farm was all about when emergencies such as this arose, and despite the long, tiring hours on her feet, she loved every moment of it.

The situation was no better and no worse for Ken Rudman at Waverley, and when he finally arrived to make a full report to Adam he looked as tired and haggard as everyone else. His car came up the drive just as Lisa was returning to the house with the twins after a promised swim, and she sent them inside to change as Ken climbed out of his car and approached her.

'Hello, Lisa,' he smiled a little wearily, jerking his thumb in the direction of the house. 'Is the boss in?'

'I don't know. He went out early this morning on an inspection tour, and I haven't seen him return.'

'You're not still angry with me, are you?'

'I was never angry with you, Ken,' she assured him hastily.

'Have you forgiven me, then?'

'There's nothing to forgive,' she smiled at him, but he caught hold of her arm as she stepped past him to continue on her way up to the house.

'Don't go yet. Sit here with me for a moment.' He drew her down on to the rough wooden bench beneath the eucalyptus tree, and looked at her closely for a few seconds before he said: 'You're very lovely, Lisa, and this isn't just flattery.'

Lisa looked away uncomfortably, and murmured something appropriate, but Ken placed his fingers beneath her chin and forced her to look at him again.

'I've never developed such an instant crush on any girl before, and it isn't going to be easy just being your friend, you know,' he told her with a seriousness she had not attributed to him, and she knew that somehow she had to make him understand that there could never be anything between them.

'Ken, I'm sorry, but——'

'I know,' he interrupted, releasing her. 'It's eyes on and hands off, but I'd like to know who's the lucky guy. I mean I'd like to know who beat me to it.'

'You're mistaken. There's no one.'

'My old dad always says that when a girl blushes you know she's lying,' Ken told her with a touch of humour in his glance, and her hands flew instantly to her hot cheeks.

'Your old dad must know a lot about women, and their ways,' she laughed off her embarrassment.

'You could say so, yes,' he nodded thoughtfully. 'He was married twice after my mother died, but both marriages ended in divorce. Now he just lives with whichever woman takes his fancy. It's less complicated that way.'

'I suppose so,' Lisa agreed reluctantly, 'but it doesn't offer the woman much security.'

'Most women couldn't care less about security these days,' Ken replied airily. 'They've stepped up into responsible positions once held only by men, and they've built up a secure future for themselves which doesn't necessitate security in marriage. To be tied to a man is an encumbrance, and a husband will inevitably display his chauvinistic tendencies one day by objecting to his wife going out to work.'

An involuntary smile plucked at her lips. 'Are you a chauvinist?'

'I don't think so,' he laughed, pushing a hand through his unruly hair, 'but I still like the idea of coming home at night to a wife who'll soothe me by discussing the little things that make life worthwhile, instead of a woman who's intent upon throwing facts and figures at me to impress me with her knowledge.'

'You *are* a bit of a chauvinist, then,' she teased lightly.

'I think most men are, although some are bighearted enough to pretend they're not,' he confessed with a boyish grin, and then he was serious again. 'You still haven't told me who the lucky man in your life is.'

Lisa plucked a leaf off the eucalyptus tree and crushed it between her fingers to inhale the fragrance. 'Don't ask me, Ken.'

'Is it such a terrible secret?'

'There's no one, and I don't——'

Her voice faltered at the sound of familiar footsteps crunching on the gravel, and she looked up quickly to see Adam walking towards them. Tiredness was etched deeply about his mouth and eyes, and the streaks of grey at his temples seemed to be more prominent than before, but as those dark eyes met hers, she lowered her lashes swiftly to hide the tender concern that lay in their depths.

'Did you want to see me, Rudman?' he demanded abruptly, and Ken rose instantly to his feet.

'Yes, sir.'

'I'll be in my study. Make it snappy, will you?'

'Yes, sir.' They watched in silence as Adam's tall, khaki-clad figure strode towards the house, then, as he disappeared behind the honeysuckle hedge, Ken turned to Lisa and stared at her intently. 'It's him, isn't it?'

Lisa rose to her feet abruptly. 'You'd better not keep him waiting. He hasn't been in a very good mood these past two days.'

'He isn't the marrying kind, Lisa,' Ken persisted urgently. 'When a man reaches his age without taking the plunge, then you can be sure he never will.'

'More advice from your old dad?' she mocked him a little tritely, but Ken merely shook his head.

'You're wasting your time, Lisa.'

'And you're wasting Mr Vandeleur's,' she retorted sharply, determined now to end this conversation.

'Just remember what I said,' he warned her, then raised his hand in salute. 'See you.'

Disturbed that Ken should have guessed her closely guarded secret so easily, Lisa remained where she was for a few minutes longer to control the rapid, uncomfortable beat of her heart. If her feelings had been that obvious to Ken, then how obvious were they to Adam, and anyone else who cared to notice?

Her colour came and went as she wrestled with this burning question. There was nothing she could do now about Ken knowing, but she would certainly have to be more careful in future unless she wanted everyone to know exactly how foolish she had been.

Lisa groaned inwardly and hurried inside to shower and change before lunch, and a half hour in Josh and Kate's company proved to be an excellent diversion for her thoughts, but their subdued behaviour at the luncheon table made her realise once again that something had to be done about the relationship which existed between the twins and their uncle. They stole furtive glances at him from time to time, and the fear and longing in their eyes was almost unbearable to witness.

Erica Vandeleur was watching her grandchildren as well, as she had been doing since Lisa had brought the situation to her notice, but, when she met Lisa's beseeching glance across the table, she shook her grey head slightly, indicating clearly that this was not the right moment to broach the subject.

Adam looked up then, and his mother hastily handed round the bowl of salad.

'What about you, Josh ... and you, Kate,' she said when both Adam and Lisa had declined. 'More salad?'

The twins merely shook their curly heads as children often do, and before Lisa could correct them Adam demanded harshly, 'Where are your manners?'

They literally shrank in their chairs as they chorussed hastily, 'No, thank you, Gran.'

Adam's curt nod indicated that the matter was settled as far as he was concerned, but their flushed cheeks and quivering lips made Lisa's mouth set in a determined line. She would speak to Adam, and soon, she decided, but right now she had to get the twins upstairs to their room for their afternoon nap.

That evening, after dinner, Lisa went for her usual walk. Her hip had improved considerably since her arrival on the farm, but it was not her hip she was thinking of at that moment. She was thinking of the twins, and what to do about the tense situation between them and their uncle. Would he take kindly to any advice she might care to offer? she wondered distractedly, but Rolf bounded up to her out of the shadows at that moment and, as she stroked and patted him fondly, the object of her thoughts materialised before her eyes.

'A girl should never be allowed to dream alone in the moonlight.'

'I wasn't dreaming,' she contradicted Adam's mocking statement as he fell into step beside her, but the unfortunate choice of a word took her back instantly to the night of the storm when he had awakened her from her terrifying nightmare, and the colour surged painfully into her cheeks as she recalled the way she had sought comfort in his arms.

'I interrupted a very serious discussion between Rudman and yourself this morning. Were you thinking of him, perhaps?'

Lisa recovered herself swiftly at the harsh mockery in his voice. 'Ken and I weren't discussing anything of importance. It was Josh and Kate I was thinking of.'

'Really?'

His sarcasm sparked off her anger, but, as she stopped and turned to face him, she knew that she would have to tread cautiously if she hoped to have any success. Should she speak to him now, or should she wait? she wondered nervously as she saw him clench his pipe between his teeth and thrust his hands into the pockets of his corded pants. He looked so formidable; so unapproachably austere at that moment. Did she dare speak to him about something which was really no concern of hers?

'You've suddenly gone very quiet, Lisa. I wonder why,' he remarked thoughtfully, and Lisa scraped her flagging courage together and plunged into speech.

'Adam, I know that—that you've been extremely busy for some time now, but——'

'But?'

She swallowed nervously. 'I think you ought to know that the twins feel you don't care for them.'

'That's utter nonsense!' he thundered, knocking out his pipe against the stem of a tree with such violence that she expected it to snap in two at any moment. 'I admit that initially I didn't fancy the idea of having my household disrupted, but they're my brother's children, and I'm their guardian.'

'They accept you as their uncle and guardian, but they need a little more than that,' she returned quietly. 'They need to know that they're loved as well.'

'Do they?' he demanded sarcastically. 'And what do you suggest I do about it? Wear a placard around my neck, or make a public declaration?'

'I wouldn't suggest anything as drastic as that.' Lisa hesitated, not sure whether she should continue under the circumstances, but his gesture of impatience made her press on. 'Spend a little more time with them so that they may get to know you, not only as their authoritative uncle and guardian, but also as their friend, and someone who cares. When you've done that, the rest will come naturally.'

'You think so?'

'I'm certain of it.'

Adam's expression became slightly cynical in the moonlight. 'Do you make a habit of trying to solve people's problems for them?'

'Don't mock my efforts, Adam,' she rebuked him, curbing her anger with difficulty. 'I'm fond of the children, and I ... I'd like to help.'

Adam was silent for a moment, and there was all at once an element of danger in the warm, sultry night air when he asked, 'Are you fond of me too?'

Lisa stiffened and withdrew from him mentally as far as she could. 'You're my employer.'

'And that puts me in a category out of reach?'

'I wasn't aware that I was trying to reach you,' she stated coldly and, reacting upon the warnings that flashed through her mind, she turned and walked away from him, but Adam seemed to anticipate her movements, and his hands gripped her shoulders, drawing her relentlessly towards him until her back rested against his chest.

'Did it ever occur to you that *I* might be trying to reach *you*?' he asked with his lips close to her ear.

She could not speak for a moment as that familiar current of awareness flowed from his hands throughout her entire body, but when his lips began to explore the sensitive cord of her neck, she could no longer remain passive beneath his touch and she struggled for release.

'Please ... don't,' she begged unsteadily, but his arms encircled her from behind, trapping her against his hard, muscular body.

'I like your perfume,' he murmured, nuzzling her neck and sending a shiver of unwanted delight through her.

'I don't use perfume.'

'Whatever it is, then, it smells good,' he insisted, quite unperturbed by her struggles as he continued the deliberate exploration of her neck and shoulder where the narrow strap of her dress had already been brushed aside by the persistence of his lips.

Lisa shut her eyes and fought against the clamouring

emotions he aroused in her, but her resistance was ebbing swiftly as she made one last, desperate effort to free herself.

'Please, Adam,' she gasped, pushing at those arms holding her so effortlessly. 'Leave me alone!'

'You're asking the impossible,' he seemed to growl in her ear, and then she was swung round to face him.

'Let me go!' she cried frantically as his lips descended on hers, and then her pleas were silenced effectively by the sensual pressure of his warm mouth.

Her senses were reeling, and the desire to respond was very nearly overpowering, but she *had* to fight against it. She dared not let him see how completely he had her within his power, and she would not be his plaything when Willa was not around to amuse him.

The thought of Willa suddenly threw a blanket over the fire of her emotions and, with an unexpected burst of strength, she thrust him from her.

'How dare you!' she cried in anguish, and before she could stop herself she had struck him a sharp blow across the cheek that left the palm of her hand tingling.

The sound echoed like a pistol shot in the velvety darkness of the garden and, horrified at what she had done, she tried to make amends, but a paralysing numbness had taken possession of her vocal chords, and she could only stand and stare up at him helplessly while the look on his face, as he towered over her, sent a shiver of cold fear up her spine.

'No one slaps my face and gets away with it,' he said in a dangerously calm voice. 'Not even you, Lisa.'

She tried again to speak, to ward off the terrifying results of her unforgivable action, but her voice failed her at the most critical moment, and his anger, when he finally released it, was something she hoped never to experience again.

With her arms pinned firmly at her sides, his mouth took hers with a savage brutality that could not have been more painful had he retaliated by striking her, and, as she sagged against him limply, he added insult to injury by running his hands over her body in a way that told her exactly what he thought of her.

The punishment ended at last when she tasted the salt of her tears in her mouth, and for a moment she stood swaying before him with a rawness in her heart that could not be assuaged.

'Now you have reason to strike me,' Adam stated harshly, his voice jarring against her jangled nerves and, turning from him with a choked cry, she fled across the garden and stumbled up the steps into the house.

She reached her room somehow, thanking heaven that Erica Vandeleur was not about, and then the deluge of tears could no longer be checked. Lying across the bed, she stifled her sobs in the pillow and wept like a child. She had deserved to be punished, but she had not deserved those insults conveyed through his hands on her body, and the entire incident left her feeling degraded, humiliated, and terribly empty.

CHAPTER TEN

IT rained incessantly during the next few days, which was quite extraordinary weather for the Karoo, and the seemingly barren veld came alive with a colourful assortment of flowers that not only amazed Lisa, but won her over completely to become as enchanted as Erica Vandeleur had warned she would.

None of this made any difference, however, to the fact that she would eventually have to leave Fairview to return to the city. It was an unpleasant thought, but what hurt her most was the chilly politeness Adam had subjected her to since that night she had so unforgivably slapped his face. She had failed in her plight for the twins' sake, she had told herself then, but despite her initial misgivings there appeared to be a slight change in Adam's attitude towards them, and this afforded her one small spark of joy in her now dismal existence.

The children were wary of him at first, and Adam's tight-lipped expression at times was neither promising, nor encouraging, but with Christmas less than a month away, the subject of suitable gifts was discussed over afternoon tea in the garden one Sunday. Kate and Josh could not make up their minds what they wanted for Christmas when their grandmother questioned them tentatively, and the discussion almost ended in an argument between the twins. It was at this point that Adam decided to take part in the conversation.

'What about a pony?' he suggested casually, and two pairs of brown eyes were turned on him instantly; eyes filled with wary uncertainty.

141

'A pony?' Josh asked hesitantly. 'A real pony?'

'A real pony,' Adam insisted, stretching his long legs out before him and sucking thoughtfully on his pipe. 'One for yourself, and one for Kate, then you could both learn to ride.'

There was a frightful little pause, and Lisa held her breath. Adam had taken a gigantic step in the right direction, but the outcome depended entirely on the children's response.

'Do you really mean that, Uncle Adam?' Kate broke the silence by questioning his sincerity.

'Do I usually say things that I don't mean?'

'No ... I don't think so,' Kate replied hesitantly, lapsing into silence, and it was Josh who finally asked, 'Will you teach us to ride, Uncle Adam?'

There was again that tense little silence, but a flicker of a smile was softening Adam's stern features as he said: 'If you're good, yes.'

'Yippee!' the twins shouted excitedly, while Lisa slowly expelled the air from her lungs.

The ice was broken and, as the twins clambered confidently on to his lap to perch themselves on his knees, Lisa and Erica Vandeleur exchanged a smile of relief. It seemed to Lisa as if the impossible had been achieved, and the sun was suddenly a little brighter on that warm summer's day beneath the shady oak.

It took a little time adjusting to the sight of Adam with the twins in his arms, smiling with tolerant amusement at their exuberant display of affection, but it also looked so perfectly right. There was, surprisingly, no awkwardness in his manner towards them, and Lisa could quite easily imagine him sitting there with his own children on his lap; children with dark hair like Adam's and green eyes like Willa's.

A red mist of pain flashed before her eyes, and jealousy,

as she had never known it before, seared through her agonisingly, but she made a supreme effort to control herself by concentrating on the conversation taking place.

'Uncle Adam, you're the best uncle in the whole world,' Kate announced shyly, kissing him on the cheek, and his heavy eyebrows rose in surprise and amusement.

'Well, I don't know so much about being the best uncle in the world, because it took some very straight talking from a certain someone to make me realise that I haven't been much of an uncle lately.' His eyes met Lisa's, and she knew instinctively that this was his way of thanking her, but there was also something else in those dark, compelling eyes; something she tried vainly to grasp even after he had lowered his gaze to the twins once more. 'What about going for a swim?'

'Oh, yes! Please!' they cried excitedly as they jumped off his lap. 'Let's go and change.'

'I thought Willa was expecting you over at their place this afternoon,' Erica Vandeleur wanted to know as he rose from his chair to follow the children inside.

'I'll give her a ring and tell her that I can't make it,' he shrugged it off, and then he was striding out across the lawn towards the house.

'That won't please Willa very much,' Mrs Vandeleur remarked caustically when he was out of earshot. 'We've known her since she was a child, but lately she seems to think Adam belongs to her, and she won't take kindly to being stood up for the twins.'

Lisa said nothing, but she wondered how long Erica Vandeleur would still have to wait before she was told of the deepening relationship between her son and Willa Jackson.

'Perhaps they're waiting for Christmas to make the announcement, and ... Oh, God!' she thought despairingly. 'I wish I were dead!'

*

Two weeks before Christmas Lisa was called to Adam's study one evening after dinner and, as she sat facing him across the wide expanse of his desk, she wondered nervously what she could have done that it should warrant a private confrontation in his study, but Adam appeared to be in no hurry to enlighten her, and she was forced to wait with barely concealed patience while he took his time lighting his pipe to his satisfaction.

'I've invited your mother and your aunt to spend a few weeks over Christmas and the New Year with us,' he said at last, blowing a cloud of smoke into the air and filling the room with the pungent aroma of his brand of tobacco.

'You've *what*?' she asked incredulously, leaning forward and gripping the arms of her chair.

'You heard me.'

'Why?' she demanded, making no effect to hide the fact that his statement had startled her. 'Why have you invited them?'

'We intend to have a very quiet Christmas, but my mother would very much like to see your aunt again, so I suggested inviting her to spend the festive season with us. I also decided that you might like to have your mother here with you.'

'Oh,' she said foolishly, still finding it a little difficult to grasp the situation. 'Have they ... have they accepted?'

'I received a letter from your mother and your aunt this morning. They'll be delighted to come, and they'll be arriving next week as suggested.'

'Oh.'

'You don't sound too happy about it,' he observed quietly, his eyes narrowed and intent upon her through a haze of smoke.

'I don't know what I feel at the moment. I——' She bit her lip and clasped her hands tightly in her lap. She *did* know suddenly how she felt. She did not want her mother and her aunt there on the farm with her. They were the two people closest to her, and they knew her too well. They would guess her secret, and would know of her utter misery. She did not want that, but it was too late to do anything about it. 'It was kind of you to invite them,' she said at last, keeping her eyes lowered.

'I do things for a purpose, and never out of kindness,' Adam retorted harshly, rising to his feet and kicking his chair back with such violence that she jumped nervously.

'What was the purpose of your invitation, then?'

Adam stood with his back to her, staring out of the window with one hand clenched, while the other was thrust into the pocket of his immaculate grey slacks, and he took so long to answer her that she was beginning to think that he had not heard her, but he turned to face her at last and said with a shrug, 'Most people enjoy being with their families at Christmas time, and I have no reason to believe that you're any different from the others.'

'You did it for me, then?'

His lips twisted into a semblance of a smile. 'Not entirely.'

'You're confusing me,' she admitted, a hand fluttering to her brow as she tried to fathom his reasoning.

'All you have to do is accept the fact that your mother and your aunt will be spending Christmas here with you, and leave it at that,' he said with a hint of familiar impatience, and as she stared at him silently she realised that his kindness, or whatever he wanted to call it, had paved the way for her to dispense with something which had lain heavily on her conscience for some time.

'Are you—are you in a hurry to get back to whatever you were doing?' she asked haltingly as she stared at the papers strewn across his desk.

'Not if there's something you want to discuss with me,' he replied, walking round to her side of the desk and seating himself on the corner of it. He waited, but as Lisa searched frantically for the right words, he said impatiently: 'Well? Is it so difficult to say what's on your mind?'

'I—I'm not finding it—it difficult to say what's on my mind,' she began haltingly, conscious of his eyes on her face, and of the nervous flutter at the pit of her stomach. 'It's not what I have to say that's so difficult, but I haven't had the—the opportunity to speak to you alone since— since the other night, and—and when there's a delay in—in doing what you have to do, it's always a little difficult finding the right words, but——' She clenched her hands tightly in her lap and raised her troubled glance to his. 'I owe you an apology, Adam. I—I don't usually make a habit of—of slapping people's faces.' Horrifyingly close to tears, she lowered her eyes again hastily as she murmured, 'I'm sorry.'

A long, uncomfortable silence followed, then Adam said quietly, 'A girl usually slaps a man's face when she feels he's insulted her, and, initially, it hadn't been my intention to do that.'

'I—I know,' she whispered, keeping her head lowered as she blinked away the moisture in her eyes.

'What happened afterwards is regrettable,' he continued, 'but I'd like to know what had prompted you to such violence.'

Lisa's heart lurched uncomfortably. To explain would mean revealing how she felt about him, and that was something she had to avoid, so she shook her head and muttered, 'I can't explain.'

'Because you don't want to? Or because there really was no reason for your behaviour?'

'Because I can't explain! I just *can't*!' she exclaimed, jumping to her feet in a panic and darting round the chair to get away from him.

The quick rise and fall of her small breasts beneath her cashmere sweater conveyed the extent of her agitation, and as the silence lengthened between them her eyes were relentlessly drawn to his. In the subdued light of the desk lamp his eyes were almost black as they burned into hers. She tried to look away, but she could not, and she stood there helpless, like a bird caught in the hypnotic glance of a snake.

'Your eyes fascinate me,' his deep voice vibrated along her nerves, bringing her out of her trance-like state. 'Did you know that they become a deep violet blue when you're excited?'

She trembled, almost as if he had touched her. 'Please, Adam, stop it!'

His eyebrows rose mockingly. 'Has no one ever told you that before?'

'No,' she admitted, taking several deep breaths to steady herself.

'How unobservant of Rory what's-his-name,' Adam remarked a little dryly and, intercepting her quick glance at the door, he stepped across the room and opened it. 'You're free to go if you want to,' he said, leaning against the doorframe with his thumbs hooked into the narrow belt hugging his hips.

She was free to go, yes, but to do so she would have to brush past him. She took a few hesitant steps towards the door, and then stopped, her pulses drumming out a nervous tattoo, and an unconscious plea in her eyes.

'My God!' he exclaimed harshly, kicking the door shut. 'I swore I'd never touch you again, but when you look at me like that——!'

He broke off sharply, his eyes a mask of unfathomable anger, and then what she had feared happened. He swept her into his arms and his mouth came down on hers with the precision of an eagle swooping down on its defenceless prey. Like the captured animal, she knew that it was useless to struggle, and she remained passive in his arms, fighting a desperate battle with herself as she endeavoured to keep her lips unresponsive beneath the relentless, demanding pressure of his. It was virtually an impossible task, when all she really wanted to do was to surrender herself to the ecstasy of his lips and arms, but she dared not. She *had* to remember that he was merely amusing himself with her, and, even though the temptation to respond was increasing alarmingly, she *had* to think of Willa.

Adam raised his head suddenly. 'Kiss me back, damn you!'

'No!' She raised protesting hands to ward off his descending lips. 'You have no right to make such demands upon me. '*You* know it, and *I* know it.'

'What the devil are you talking about?' he thundered at her, releasing her so suddenly that she almost fell.

'You don't need me to explain the situation to you. You *know* what I'm talking about.'

'I'm damned if I do,' he almost shouted at her, 'but we'll let the matter pass for the moment. I'm not in the mood to try and fathom the workings of a woman's mind.' He jerked open the door and stepped away from it this time. 'You may go, Lisa. I don't think we have anything further to say to each other at present.'

Something was terribly wrong, she realised suddenly. But what? She took a hesitant step towards him. 'Adam ...'

'Go, Lisa!' he ordered harshly, waving his arm towards the door. 'Go before I do, or say something that I might regret later. Heaven knows, I've taken just about as much as a man can stand, and at this moment I'd like nothing better than to shake some sense into you.'

Lisa's eyes widened at the dark fury on his rugged features, then she turned and walked out of his study, closing the door softly behind her. In the passage she paused for a moment, confused and bewildered by something she did not understand, but, as she heard something that sounded like Adam's fist coming down heavily on to his desk, she walked quickly down the passage and crossed the darkened hall towards the stairs.

Tomorrow, perhaps, she would understand the reason for his deliberate obtuseness; tomorrow, when her body was not still tingling from the pressure of his arms, she would be able to sort out the muddled thoughts cascading through her mind. But tonight there was only the pain and confusion, and the longing for something she could not have.

Celia Moreau and Molly Anstey arrived one afternoon the following week and, when her aunt's dusty old Peugeot came up the drive, Lisa, the twins, and Erica Vandeleur were there to welcome them to Fairview. Adam, too, came walking round the corner of the house at that moment, and he stood aside patiently while Lisa was hugged and kissed effusively by her mother and her aunt. Celia Moreau opened up her motherly arms to Josh and Kate, and they went into them with a surprising lack of shyness, but Adam's geniality in welcoming her family surprised Lisa most of all. The servants were called to take care of their suitcases and the car, and, flanked by Adam and Erica Vandeleur, the two women were ushered out of the scorching sun and into the coolness of the house.

Lisa and the twins followed more slowly, but there was a puzzled frown on her usually smooth brow when she later saw her mother chatting softly to Adam over tea. Their discussion appeared to be of a serious nature, but Lisa noticed that Adam obviously had difficulty in hiding his amusement at times. There seemed to be an easy familiarity between them, as if they had known each other for some time, and Lisa suddenly envied her mother her self-assurance.

'Oh, it's wonderful to be here again, Erica,' Molly Anstey sighed, drawing Lisa's attention away from her mother and Adam for a while. 'It's been so many years, and yet it seems like yesterday to me,' her aunt continued, leaning back in her chair and looking about her with interest. 'Your niece and I used to fight over whose turn it was to eat the warm crust of the freshly-baked bread, and then we used to plaster it with fresh farm butter, but I remember best of all how we used to go haring across the veld on horseback.' Molly laughed reminiscently. 'I wonder sometimes how we managed not to get ourselves seriously injured!'

Erica Vandeleur smiled with a touch of wry humour on her face. 'You and Peggy were both rather wild in those days.'

'Tell me about Peggy,' said Molly, turning to the older woman seated in the upright stinkwood chair beside her own. 'We lost contact somehow when she married that Austrian of hers and went overseas.'

The twins became restless at this stage and, unnoticed, Lisa took them outside.

'Is your mother also a teacher?' they wanted to know as Lisa walked with them down the drive and out across the veld to the nearest camp where they could watch the sheep being herded into a kraal for the night.

'My mother isn't a teacher, but my aunt is,' Lisa told them, placing her arms protectively about them when they climbed up on to the gate and perched there precariously.

'I like your mother,' Kate announced. 'She's so pretty, and she smells nice too.'

'Just like you, Lisa,' Josh added, kissing Lisa unexpectedly on the cheek.

'Why, thank you,' she laughed happily, tightening her

arms about them affectionately. 'It will make my mother very happy to know that you like her.'

'There's Uncle Adam,' Josh exclaimed suddenly, and the twins waved excitedly.

Adam, with his broad-brimmed hat pulled characteristically over his eyes, raised his hand and waved back, then the black stallion gathered speed and galloped off in the direction of the small hill behind the outbuildings. There was a large grazing paddock beyond that hill, but the Jacksons' farm also lay in that direction, and the tantalising question was ... to which would he be going in such a hurry?

'I wish it was Christmas already, then we could go with Uncle Adam on our ponies when he rides into the veld,' Josh sighed impatiently.

'You won't have to wait much longer,' Lisa pacified him, her wistful eyes following Adam's imposing figure on that magnificent horse until he was out of sight. 'Christmas is just a few days away, but then you'll first have to learn to ride before you will be allowed to ride with your uncle.'

'We'll learn very quickly,' Kate said seriously, and Lisa laughed as she helped them off the gate and took them back to the house.

Lisa's laughter was a little hollow, however, for the time was coming nearer for her to leave, and she would have to become accustomed to the empty vessel her life would become once she was back in the city. She would miss the twins, the late afternoon walks, the fiery sunsets, and the warm, star-studded nights, but most of all she would miss Adam. The longing for him, and for what could never be, would eat away at her relentlessly, but it had to be faced. She would bury herself in her work, like her aunt had done, and just pray that she grew too old to care.

Josh and Kate ran ahead, but Lisa followed more slowly, her limp barely noticeable now at that pace, but Lisa had been too preoccupied lately to realise that she no longer walked with the old pronounced limp. Her scars, too, were barely noticeable in the golden hue of the setting sun as it settled in her hair to form a glorious halo about the soft contours of her face, but it was not herself or her appearance she was thinking of at that moment. She was thinking of Adam; of his mockery, his cynicism, his frowns, his twisted little smiles, and the forbidden wonder of his lips and arms.

No, *no*! She must not think of him like that, she told herself fiercely, quickening her pace to catch up to the twins. She must think of him only as her employer, and the man who had found her an amusing plaything when the woman he had chosen to marry was not about. Yes, she must think of him like that; as the man who thought nothing of being unfaithful to the woman whom he had asked to share his life. He was a cad! A rake!

A cad and a rake he might be, but ... dear heaven! What did it matter *what* name she attached to him? she thought in despair. He could be the devil incarnate, and she would still love him and want him with that aching longing that was eating away at her like a corrosive canker.

'Lisa, you're not listening!' the children's agitated voices finally got through to her, and she looked down at them with a guilty start.

'I'm sorry. What were you saying?'

'Do we have to bath tonight?' Josh demanded. 'We didn't dirty ourselves today.'

'Oh, yes, you have to bath,' Lisa insisted firmly, giving them a gentle shove into the house. 'Upstairs, both of you, and into that bath, or your uncle might think twice about letting you have a pony for Christmas.'

Their sulky expressions vanished miraculously, and they ran across the hall and clambered up the stairs without further argument. Lisa glanced into the living-room as she followed them, but there was no one there and, glimpsing the time, she realised that it was later than usual. Her mother and her aunt were most probably up in their rooms changing for dinner, but there was no time for her now to drop in on them. The twins had to be bathed and fed, and then she would have to rush through a bath herself if she wanted to be on time for dinner.

When Lisa finally went downstairs, she found everyone in the living-room, and Adam gestured her into a chair beside his own while he poured her a glass of sherry. Their eyes met briefly, then she looked away and tried to still the quickening of her heartbeats as she raised her glass to her lips to sip the fiery liquid.

'Lisa, my dear, I just can't get over it,' her mother remarked when there was a lull in the conversation. 'You're looking wonderful. You're still a little on the thin side, but you're so beautifully tanned.'

'Didn't I say that the Karoo air would do wonders for you?' her aunt added mischievously, and the colour rose faintly in Lisa's cheeks.

'You did, Aunt Molly.'

'When I first suggested her coming here to Fairview, she wouldn't hear of it,' her aunt elaborated to an interested Adam, and Lisa felt her cheeks grow warmer as her aunt continued. 'Lisa said that the Karoo was hot and dusty, and far too primitive for a city girl like herself.'

Lisa drained her glass and, aware that everyone's eyes were on her at that moment, she tried to hide her embarrassment by saying tritely, 'Don't remind me of my ignorance, please, Aunt Molly.'

The women laughed, but Lisa could feel Adam's eyes burning into her like two coals of fire. 'Have you changed your mind about the Karoo, then?'

She drew the shutters on her soul and looked at him then. 'I don't think anyone could live here for a time and *not* change their mind.'

Adam's eyes were unfathomable dark pools as he said: 'If you were offered the opportunity, would you consider remaining here permanently?'

'I don't think so,' she replied instantly, shrinking from the idea of being on hand to witness his eventual marriage, and vaguely aware of the other three women in the room exchanging quick glances as she added: 'It's time I went back to teaching.'

'And to civilisation, in fact.'

'I never said that!' she reacted sharply to the hint of derisive mockery in his voice, but before either of them could say more, Erica Vandeleur rose to her feet.

'Shall we go in to dinner?'

'Good idea,' Adam agreed instantly, setting aside his empty glass and getting to his feet. 'After you, ladies.'

Erica Vandeleur led the way, and Lisa made up the rear with Adam directly behind her. She felt his eyes on her, and she tensed inwardly, fighting off the familiar sensations that quivered along her nerves.

What had he meant by asking her if she would consider remaining here permanently if she were offered the opportunity? she wondered throughout dinner. Was he thinking of finding her work somewhere in the district? Somewhere close enough, perhaps, so that she would continually run into him and Willa? Lisa shivered and thrust aside the distasteful thought. She did not want to be within a hundred-kilometre radius of him after his marriage to Willa, so there was only one way she could go. Back to Cape Town!

CHAPTER ELEVEN

LISA had the opportunity to be alone with her mother for the first time the following morning after tea had been served on the verandah. Mrs Vandeleur and Aunt Molly had excused themselves to go in search of an old family album, but an odd little silence had hovered in the air since their departure.

'More tea, Mother?' Lisa offered eventually, trying to shake off her uneasiness.

'Not at the moment, thank you, dear,' Celia Moreau declined, shifting a little uncomfortably in her chair, and then the reason for her discomfiture was explained. 'I saw Rory in town a few weeks ago. He asked for your address, and I didn't want to appear rude, so I gave it to him.' She glanced quickly at her daughter. 'Did he write to you?'

'No, Mother,' Lisa smiled wryly. 'He came here to see me instead, but I'm afraid he had a wasted journey.'

'You sent him away?'

'Yes.'

'Perhaps it was for the best,' her mother agreed seriously, and once again there was that odd little silence between them that puzzled Lisa. She stared at her mother curiously, but she appeared to be perfectly relaxed, and when their glances met, Celia smiled. 'Adam is such a nice man, don't you think?'

Lisa did not know what she had expected, but this sudden reference to Adam startled her, and she stiffened automatically. 'I suppose so, yes.'

'It was very kind of him to write and invite me here as well, don't you think?'

'Yes ... very kind,' Lisa smiled a little cynically, recalling Adam's assertion that he never did anything out of kindness, but for a purpose; a purpose she had yet to discover.

'Do you get on well with him?'

'Well enough,' Lisa replied abruptly, realising at once that she would have to be on her guard against remarks such as these.

'He seems to be such a reliable and dependable man, and not at all the kind who would ever let anyone down in a moment of crisis.'

Lisa knew her mother too well not to be aware of the intense curiosity hidden behind that supposedly casual remark, and she decided to laugh it off, as she had done so often in the past before Rory Phillips had walked in and out of her life.

'Mother, you're as transparent as cellophane!'

'Am I?' Celia Moreau asked, attempting to look blank, but Lisa was not fooled for one moment.

'You're trying, very subtly, to find out what my feelings are for Adam Vandeleur, but you're wasting your time,' Lisa accused directly, and she was surprised to see her mother go a little pink in the face.

'I was merely wondering——'

'Don't, Mother,' Lisa interrupted, hiding the pain in her heart with a convincing display of disinterest. 'Adam Vandeleur is my employer, and beyond that we have nothing in common, so don't imagine that I have developed an undying passion for him.'

'I haven't imagined anything of the kind,' her mother protested, 'but, as your mother, I'm naturally concerned about your future, and I would like to see you settled happily with someone nice and dependable.'

Lisa smiled faintly. 'I'm sure you do, Mother, but that "someone nice and dependable" won't be Adam Vandeleur.'

'Don't you like him, then?'

'Whether I like him or not makes no difference to the situation,' Lisa replied, meeting her mother's direct gaze with eyes that were carefully hooded. 'He's my employer and, as such, I respect him.'

Celia Moreau stared hard at her daughter for a moment, her disappointment obvious, but as the children came charging round the corner of the house to raid the cake tin yet again, she gestured a little helplessly with her hands.

'I think another cup of tea would do nicely now, if you don't mind.'

The subject was not mentioned again during the last two days before Christmas, but Lisa was quite aware of being observed closely whenever Adam was about. She became aloof, and deliberately arranged that she would be occupied elsewhere as much as possible when Adam was in the house. It was unavoidable that they should spend time together over the Christmas weekend, but Lisa was on her guard, and purposely submerged herself in Josh and Kate's excitement as they helped to decorate the tree in the living-room.

Lisa had not had much time to do her Christmas shopping, so her gifts had had to be carefully thought out beforehand. For her aunt there was a bottle of her favourite perfume, and for her mother the pearl earrings she had always wanted, but somehow never had the money to buy. For Mrs Vandeleur Lisa chose the genuine silk scarf she had admired in a shop window one day, and for the twins each a book on animals which she knew they would enjoy. Adam had presented a problem, though. He was her employer and probably did not expect anything from her, but she finally shook off her misgivings and decided on fine linen handkerchiefs with his initial embroidered in the one corner.

The presents were handed out on Christmas Eve, but beneath the laughter and the gaiety Lisa sensed a hint of sadness. The Vandeleur family had been tragically deprived of two of its members, and their thoughts must have gone repeatedly to the previous Christmas when they had all still been together.

Lisa's eyes filled with tears as she looked down at the twins playing quite happily on the carpet at her feet, but she blinked away the mistinesss unobtrusively. Josh and Kate had been thrilled at the concession their uncle had made which had allowed them to stay up later than usual, but when the clock on the mantelshelf struck nine Adam cleared his throat significantly.

'Can't we stay up just a little longer, Uncle Adam?' Josh begged, despite the droopiness of his eyelids, but Adam was adamant.

'If you don't go to bed now, you'll be too sleepy to ride your ponies when they arrive tomorrow.'

The twins needed no further encouragement and they hastily gathered up their presents and said goodnight. Lisa followed them upstairs, but she lingered longer than necessary after tucking them up in bed, and remained until they were asleep.

She was reluctant to go downstairs, and it was no use denying it to herself. It was wonderful having her mother and her aunt there with her, but they knew her too well not to have guessed that something was wrong. She had always discussed things with them quite openly, but her feeling for Adam was something she could not bring herself to talk about—not even to her mother.

Lisa sighed and switched off the light before leaving the children's room, but in the darkened passage she collided with someone, and her heart leapt into her throat as her hands encountered the solid, immovable wall of Adam's chest.

'I came up to see what was keeping you so long,' he said, and she could feel the heat of his steadying hands at her waist through the chiffon of her dress.

'I sat with the children until they were asleep,' she explained a little shakily, the familiar aroma of tobacco and after-shave lotion attacking her senses and making her tremble inwardly. 'I—I didn't think it would matter to anyone.'

'It mattered to me,' he stated calmly. 'I haven't had the opportunity yet to thank you for the present you gave me.'

Lisa stiffened beneath his hands, shying away from the sudden intimacy that sprang up between them in the darkness, but before she could say anything, Adam was kissing her quite thoroughly on her trembling lips.

'That was just to say thank you,' he said in that infuriatingly calm manner when he released her. 'Now we'd better go downstairs or everyone will think I'm lost as well.'

Lisa said nothing, deciding to ignore the incident, but her legs were shaking beneath her as they descended the stairs, and she would have tripped on the bottom step had Adam's hand not gripped her elbow so firmly. She had a vague suspicion that her cheeks were flushed when they entered the living-room, but, for once, the three women were too engrossed in conversation to spare her more than a cursory glance.

'More wine, ladies?' Adam offered, and the glasses were quickly refilled.

Lisa drank hers slowly, allowing the faintly intoxicating drink to steady her nerves while she watched her mother's animated face as the three women exchanged memories. She looked happy and contented, Lisa thought, but the past five years had not been easy for her mother since her father's death. There had not been much in the way of insurance, and Lisa had still had two years at university to get through before she could earn a living for herself, so her mother had had to go out to work. Her typing had become rusty after years of being a mother and housewife, but she had found a job as a typist/clerk in a clothing store, and when the house was sold they at least had something to fall back on in times of trouble. There was now no necessity for her mother to work, but she had stayed on at the store, and she was now quite happy in her position as the manager's private secretary.

'It's hot inside,' Adam interrupted her thoughts. 'Shall we go out on to the verandah?' Lisa hesitated, but Adam rose to his feet and leaned over her slightly. 'Come on, don't look so scared.'

'I'm not scared.'

'Then prove it,' he challenged, straightening and holding out his hand, palm upwards.

She stared at that strong, beautifully-shaped hand for a moment, her nerves tightening at the pit of her stomach, then she placed her hand in his and allowed him to draw her to her feet.

'Just breathe that air,' he said, taking a deep breath as he drew her out on to the verandah and towards the cane chairs. 'Will you miss all this when you have to return to the city?'

'I shall miss it very much,' she admitted, trying to relax in her chair while her glance went involuntarily to the stars glittering so brightly in the dark, velvety sky.

'You could stay, you know.'

'As what?' she demanded a little cynically. 'As an extra farm-hand, perhaps?'

'Perhaps,' he laughed shortly, 'but I had something far

more satisfying and rewarding in mind.'

Lisa stiffened at the odd inflection in his voice, and she glanced at him quickly. Seated in the moonlight beside her, he appeared to be calm and relaxed, but she knew that every muscle in that large frame was geared for action at the slightest provocation.

'I don't think I want to know, thank you,' she said abruptly.

'You're not even a little bit curious?'

'No, I'm not.'

'A pity,' he murmured, stretching himself out in his chair and turning so that he could see her more clearly. 'I was so certain you would be interested.'

Lisa stared down at her hands locked so tightly in her lap. 'I have the feeling that you're mocking me for some reason, Adam.'

'Teasing, little one. Not mocking,' he corrected her softly, and she raised her uncertain glance to his.

'Why should you want to do that?'

'To entice you out of that shell of yours,' he announced a little harshly. 'You've crawled so deep into it lately that I'm beginning to despair for you.'

'There's no need for you to concern yourself about me. It's comfortable in that shell of mine, and I'm quite happy, thank you,' she told him coldly.

'*Are* you happy, Lisa?'

The question was asked softly, and with a certain sincerity that made her want to cry out, 'No, no, I'm not happy,' but instead she said stiffly: 'I'm as happy as anyone can expect to be.'

'That sounds like the lament of an embittered old maid.'

Her laughter bubbled unexpectedly past her lips. 'I suppose it does.'

'You'll never be an old maid, Lisa,' he said, leaning forward in his chair as he held her nervous glance. 'And bitterness doesn't suit a mouth like yours that was made exclusively for kissing.'

She shrank from him mentally and physically. 'I wish you wouldn't say things like that.'

'My God, I'd like to do more than just *say* things like that to you!' he exploded. 'I'd like to kiss you out of that shell of yours until you become a living, vibrant woman again.'

'Adam!' she exclaimed in a shocked voice as she jumped to her feet, the suggested intimacy of his statement making her treacherous body tingle responsively.

'Sit down,' he said quietly, but Lisa much preferred to seek the safety of the living-room where their conversation would have to be limited to impersonal subjects.

'I think——'

'*Sit down!*' he repeated in a harsh, deadly voice, and Lisa found herself obeying, albeit reluctantly. 'I wish I knew why you're always so quick to take offence,' he continued a little more gently.

'You have no right to speak to me the way you do,' she replied unsteadily, keeping her eyes lowered to her hands.

'You've said that before, and I'd like to know why you feel I have no right to speak to you in the way I do.'

'Because you're engaged to Willa,' the words sprang to her lips, but she bit them back forcibly, and said instead: 'Because you're my employer.'

'Is that the only reason?'

Lisa's heart leapt wildly, and fear of her feelings being discovered made her resort to anger. 'Must we pursue this subject?'

'Don't answer my question with another.'

'Why are you so persistent?' she demanded exasperatedly.

'Because I'm trying to find out why you shy away from me whenever I come close to discussing something personal, while I know damn well that you enjoy my kisses.'

She sucked her breath in sharply, but she regained control of herself and asked casually, 'Is it a crime to enjoy a man's kisses without wanting it to go further than that?'

'You damn little liar!' His voice was like thunder, low and threatening before the storm, and her nerves reacted violently as he gripped the arms of her chair and brought his harsh face within centimetres of her own. 'I've a good mind to prove to you just how much of a liar you are, but it would most probably shock your prim little soul to such an extent that you'd never recover.'

The moonlight played across his face a little cruelly, accentuating the greyness at his temples, the deep grooves running from nose to mouth, and the shadowy cleft in the square, resolute jaw, but it was the hard, angry glitter in his eyes, and the tightness about that often sensual mouth that frightened her most. Would he carry out his threat and prove, beyond doubt, just how susceptible she was to his lovemaking, or was it merely a threat he had no intention of carrying out?

Lisa was not too sure, but she knew she had to break the angry silence between them and, with her heart drumming louder than the sound of the crickets in the undergrowth, she said softly, almost pleadingly, 'Don't you think this conversation has gone far enough?'

'Yes, you're right,' he snapped, moving away from her almost as if he could not bear her near him. '*Quite* far enough.'

The atmosphere was strained between them when they returned to the living-room, and when the clock crawled closer to midnight without anyone showing any sign of going to bed, Lisa pleaded a headache and went up to her room.

Upset, hurt and bewildered, she tried not to think of her conversation with Adam, but it was useless. Her mind was in an unhappy turmoil. Why did he deliberately go out of his way to hurt her? Why could he not leave her alone? Why did he persist in seeking her out when he knew that he was practically engaged to Willa? Was he such a rake that a commitment of such a serious nature meant nothing to him?

Question after question swivelled through her mind, but to none of them could she find an answer, and she finally groaned into her pillow, 'Oh, God, I wish I could understand!'

She tried to analyse Adam's behaviour, but the more she tried, the more bewildered she became until at last she was forced to relinquish the effort, and slipped into a troubled sleep.

Lisa was awakened early on Christmas morning with the twins barging noisily into her room.

'Let's get dressed. Quick!' they begged, bouncing excitedly on her bed and pulling at the sheets. 'We want to go and see if the ponies have come.'

'Then you'd better get out of here so I can get dressed first,' Lisa announced sleepily, stifling a yawn, and the twins hurried out again, slamming the door behind them in their excitement.

In a paddock close to the homestead, they later came across two Shetland ponies standing side by side as they nibbled at the grass, and raised their heads to toss their manes proudly as Lisa approached with the children.

'Oooh ... they're beautiful!' the twins cooed excitedly as the ponies moved away a little warily, their brown coats smooth and shiny in the sunshine. 'Can we ride them now?'

Lisa shook her head firmly. 'You'll have to wait for your uncle.'

'I'm here,' a deep voice announced, and she swung round to see Adam coming towards them with Petrus following behind him, carrying two small saddles. Hatless, and in brown pants and beige sweater instead of his usual khaki, Adam looked strikingly different, and her heart skipped an involuntary beat at the sight of him, but he afforded her no more than a brief glance. 'Are you both ready for your first lesson?'

'Yes, yes,' the twins chorused. 'Can we help Petrus saddle the ponies?'

'Yes, if you like,' Adam agreed readily, 'but be careful.'

The children climbed through the wooden railings with the dark-skinned man who was Adam's most trusted worker on the farm, and Lisa could not prevent herself from smiling at their eagerness.

'It's Christmas Day,' Adam announced quietly beside her and, as she glanced up at him quickly, she saw his hand extended towards her. 'Do we call a truce?'

'Yes, of course,' she replied without hesitation, and her hand almost disappeared in his brief, warm clasp.

Amusement lurked in his eyes suddenly as he asked wryly, 'Do you think we'll manage to keep it up for one whole day?'

'I shall certainly try,' she smiled humorously, her eyes sparkling like clear pools of fathomless water. 'And you?'

He touched her cheek lightly with his fingers. 'I could manage anything, little one, when you look at me like that, and smile.'

Lisa felt her cheeks grow warm and she looked beyond him. 'I think the children are becoming impatient.'

'So am I, Lisa,' he smiled a little crookedly as he swung

himself over the rail into the paddock. 'So am I.'

With her eyes narrowed against the sun, she stared after him as he walked with those long, familiar strides towards the children, and helped them to mount. What had he meant? she wondered frowningly as Josh and Kate's riding lesson began in earnest. Had he perhaps been referring to his own impatience to set a date for his marriage to Willa?

Lisa hastily clamped down on her thoughts as pain stabbed at her heart. She would never understand Adam, and it was futile to try. His odd and senseless remarks lately merely served to mystify her, so she concentrated instead on the twins while they received their first riding lesson under the expert guidance of their uncle.

Adam displayed remarkable patience with the children, but they proved to be apt pupils, responding quickly to his calm instructions, and glowing with happiness whenever he praised them.

The early morning sun was stinging Lisa's arms and legs, and she was beginning to feel redundant when her aunt, returning from an early morning stroll, joined her at the fence to watch the proceedings in the paddock. The sun was too hot for Molly's delicate skin, however, and Lisa suggested that they seek shelter in the shady garden.

'I think we'd better sit down somewhere,' her aunt groaned after a while. 'I feel as though I've been trudging across the veld for hours!'

'There's a bench just under those trees,' Lisa said concernedly, taking her aunt's arm and guiding her in the right direction.

'Oh, that's better,' Molly sighed a few moments later as she lowered herself on to the wooden bench and kicked off her shoes. 'My feet are killing me!'

Lisa sat down beside her. 'Is Mother still asleep?'

'Yes, poor dear,' Molly laughed mischievously. 'I dressed quietly and sneaked out without waking her. It's such a gorgeous morning, and smell that fresh country air!' She closed her eyes and took several deep breaths. 'I just can't get enough of it.'

'It's going to be another long, hot day, and we'll begin to droop before the sun is much higher.'

'Don't remind me,' her aunt groaned, removing her scarf from her head and fastening it loosely about her throat. 'You like it here, don't you.'

It was a statement, not a question, and so typical of Molly Anstey that Lisa smiled at her humorously. 'Yes, it's hot and dusty as I once said, but I like it here very much.'

'You know, Lisa,' her aunt said after a thoughtful pause, 'Adam reminds me very much of my late husband Luke.'

The smile froze on Lisa's lips, and she tensed automatically. 'Does he?'

'Luke was just as tall and broad in the shoulders, and whenever he held me in those strong arms of his, it used to make me feel as though nothing in the world could harm me. I felt loved and protected at the same time, and Luke was the only man who ever succeeded in making me completely and utterly aware of my femininity, which was quite wonderful.' She paused and glanced curiously at Lisa. 'Doesn't Adam make you feel that way? All feminine and helpless when he looks at you?'

Lisa shrugged with affected casualness. 'I can't say I've noticed.'

'Oh, Lisa, my dear!' Molly laughed disbelievingly. 'You would have to be blind not to have noticed Adam Vandeleur's wonderful physique, and he simply oozes a virile masculinity that would make any woman's heart behave like a wild thing. I know mine does whenever I see him.'

'Aunt Molly!' Lisa exclaimed in a shocked voice.

'It's true,' her aunt stated adamantly, her mischievous glance meeting Lisa's. 'If I were twenty years younger, my girl, you wouldn't stand a chance.'

Lisa smiled stiffly and fingered the pleats of her skirt. 'What makes you think I'm interested enough to *want* a chance?'

'I've seen that certain look in your eyes whenever he is about.'

'Oh?'

Despite her efforts to appear cool and disinterested, her cheeks went pink, and Molly Anstey smiled triumphantly when her keen glance noticed Lisa's heightened colour.

'You're in love with him, aren't you,' she stated with that shrewdness Lisa had dreaded so much.

'He's my employer, Aunt Molly,' she said with a hint of hostility in her voice as she jumped to her feet and moved about agitatedly.

'So what!' her aunt exploded indignantly, patting the seat beside her with an impatient hand. 'Oh, come and sit down again, and stop being so fidgety and uppity.'

'I must go and see how the children's riding lesson is going on.'

'Adam is managing them superbly, and he's quite capable of looking after them for a while.' Grey eyes regarded Lisa intently when she resumed her seat. 'You do love him, don't you?'

'I admire and respect him,' Lisa evaded the question.

'You *should* admire and respect the man you love,' her aunt acknowledged with a look of satisfaction on her delicately-boned face, and Lisa sought refuge in anger as she had done so often lately.

'Aunt Molly, I wish you and Mother would stop prying, and trying to read something significant into my association with Adam Vandeleur,' she accused coldly. 'He's my employer, and that's all!'

Molly Anstey smiled that infuriatingly knowledgeable smile of hers. 'Do you really expect me to believe that?'

'Yes, I do,' Lisa sighed exasperatedly. 'In less than a month I shall be leaving here. I shall go back to teaching, and Adam and I won't ever see each other again.'

'And it doesn't upset you? The thought of leaving, I mean?'

'I shall miss the children very much,' Lisa answered quietly, observing her aunt's incredulous expression with a flicker of self-satisfaction. 'And now you must excuse me.'

'But Lisa ...' Molly Anstey began when Lisa was a few paces away from her.

'I don't wish to discuss the subject further,' Lisa swung round to interrupt her coldly.

The older woman was now totally confused. 'But I was so sure——'

'You were mistaken,' Lisa cut in decisively. 'You and Mother are both mistaken. Adam Vandeleur is not the man for me. See you later, Aunt Molly.'

Lisa walked blindly up to the house. From the direction of the paddock came the sound of the children's happy laughter, and quite suddenly she felt incredibly lonely. There was no place for her here at Fairview, and soon not even the twins would need her.

At the breakfast table Josh and Kate were bubbling over with enthusiasm as they related their achievements to everyone. They were perhaps a little over-confident, but Adam was forced to admit that they were doing splendidly. A new bond was being forged between himself and the children, and they responded hungrily to every word of praise he bestowed on them. He was their hero, and they would be his willing slaves, just as she would be for one glimmer of true warmth in those dark eyes of his.

When the breakfast was over, the farm-hands came to the homestead with their wives and children, and Adam gave each one a present individually. When this was done, the men and women regrouped themselves and, with Petrus and Daisy taking the lead, the singing began. They sang songs of Christmas, their voices blending and harmonising in joyful, happy songs, and for Lisa, standing on the back stoep between her mother and her aunt, it was a moment she knew she would remember for the rest of her life.

Lisa's throat tightened, and hot tears welled up into her eyes. When the time came for her to leave, she thought, she would at least be taking memories with her that no one and nothing could erase.

CHAPTER TWELVE

ADAM arranged a *braai* for the Saturday evening before Lisa's mother and aunt were due to return to Cape Town, and Willa, her parents, Ken Rudman, and several other families from neighbouring farms were invited.

On the morning of the *braai* the fires were packed, ready to be lit, and tables and chairs were carried out into the garden where Adam had erected an extension to give sufficient lighting around the fires and the tables.

Lisa helped in the kitchen with the salads for most of the day, but she felt sick at the thought that soon it would be her turn to leave, and Daisy was obviously thinking the same thoughts.

Halfway through cutting up a tomato she looked up suddenly and said: 'Miss Lisa, this old house won't be the same again without you.'

It was the nicest compliment anyone could have paid Lisa, but it also stirred up the pain, and the hopeless longing that was beginning to overwhelm her.

'Thank you, Daisy,' she smiled a little wanly. 'I've loved it here, but everything must end somewhere.'

Daisy shook her head and frowned as she resumed her task of slicing tomatoes. She muttered something about certain people not knowing the worth of something until they'd lost it, but Lisa did not dare ask for an explanation.

Later that afternoon, while Lisa was trying to decide on what to wear for the occasion, there was a knock on her door and her mother entered her room.

'You'd better hurry,' she said, taking in Lisa's state of

undress. 'Mr and Mrs Jackson and their daughter arrived a few minutes ago, and so has that nice Mr Rudman who came over for dinner on Christmas Day.'

'I can't make up my mind what to wear.'

'What about that brown pleated skirt of yours, and ...' Celia Moreau pushed aside a few dresses in the wardrobe and brought out a square, flat box lying half forgotten in the furthest corner. 'What's this?'

'Mother, don't——' Lisa began anxiously, but her mother had already opened the box and was inspecting the contents.

'Oh, but how lovely!' Celia Moreau exclaimed, running the silk blouse through her fingers. 'You must wear this with your skirt.'

'No ... I can't.'

'Why not, for goodness' sake?' her mother wanted to know, turning the blouse this way and that as she examined it carefully. 'Is there something wrong with it?'

'No, there's nothing wrong with it, but ...' Lisa swallowed hard, 'I can't wear it.'

Celia lowered the blouse and stared at her daughter in a perplexed fashion. 'But why did you buy it if you can't wear it?'

'I didn't buy it,' said Lisa before she could prevent herself, and her mother instantly grasped the situation.

'It was a gift, then?'

'Oh, Mother,' Lisa sighed exasperatedly.

'Was it a gift from Rory?' Celia persisted, but something in Lisa's expression must have given her the answer. 'It was from Adam, wasn't it?'

'I'd ripped an old cotton blouse of mine one day, and Adam decided to replace it with this,' Lisa found herself explaining patiently. 'I told him it was too expensive for me to accept, and we had quite a disagreement.'

'So you shoved it into the bottom of your wardrobe and swore never to wear it,' her mother concluded knowingly.

'Something like that, yes,' Lisa admitted grudgingly.

'Don't you think it's time you stopped being silly?' her mother rebuked her gently. 'If Adam was kind enough to give you this beautiful blouse as a gift, then the least you can do is wear it. He most probably won't even notice what you're wearing, if he's at all like other men.'

'Oh, he'll notice all right, and he'll gloat triumphantly,' Lisa snorted angrily.

'Gloat?' Celia frowned confusedly. 'I don't see why he should gloat, but does it really matter?'

Lisa stared at her mother for a moment, fighting against the desire to confide in her as she had always done, and then she shook her head. 'No, it doesn't matter. Give me that blouse.'

'I'll see you downstairs in a few minutes,' Celia Moreau smiled reassuringly, and then Lisa was alone.

She stepped into her skirt, fastening it about her narrow waist, then she slipped her arms into the sleeves of the blouse, her fingers fumbling with the tiny pearl buttons down the front and at the cuffs. She hated the idea of wearing it when she thought of the unhappy encounter she had had with Adam because of it, but the silk, admittedly, felt good against her skin.

Lisa joined everyone in the garden some minutes later, and her mother smiled approvingly when Lisa sat down in the vacant chair beside her. She had met only a few of the people present, but those she had not met introduced themselves in the friendly, jovial manner of the Karoo people. Their children kept Josh and Kate occupied with wild games on the spacious lawn until their laughter echoed across the garden, and Lisa felt free for a while from her duties.

Willa and Lisa acknowledged each other with a cool nod, but Lisa was struck almost physically by the other girl's beauty. She seldom wore anything other than slacks or riding clothes, but for this occasion Willa had chosen an emerald green silk creation that matched her eyes superbly. Her lustrous, reddish-brown hair was combed up on to her head, exposing her slender neck and beautiful tanned shoulders, but it was her air of calm confidence that drove those painful barbs into Lisa's heart. This was where Willa belonged ... on Fairview, as Adam's wife.

The fires were lit, and the men stood around them drinking their beer, while the women sipped sherry and discussed the latest bit of gossip doing the rounds in town. It was a warm night, and Lisa, feeling restless and uneasy, went into the house to see if she could help Daisy with the last-minute preparations in the kitchen, and it was there that Adam found her, bending over a plate of snacks she was preparing.

He fingered the sleeve of her blouse and smiled with more warmth than she had ever credited him with. 'I thought you were never going to wear it.'

'I changed my mind.'

'I'm glad you did,' he said abruptly, and then he winked at her quite deliberately and uncharacteristically as he walked out of the kitchen with the large dish of meat in his hands.

Lisa stared after him a little bewilderedly, not quite sure what to make of his behaviour, then she shrugged it off to continue with her task.

· The smell of woodsmoke was soon replaced by that of meat grilling on an open fire and, despite her dwindling appetite, Lisa experienced a few pangs of hunger.

'Can I help with anything?' Ken Rudman wanted to

know when he wandered into the kitchen some time later.

'Is the meat ready?'

'As ready as it will ever be,' he said, his hungry glance roaming over the salads, and Lisa promptly placed one of the loaded trays into his hands.

'Take that outside for me, will you, Ken?'

'Sure thing,' he grinned.

Lisa and Daisy followed him with the rest of the trays, and when everything was set out on the tables, Adam invited their guests to help themselves.

Willa made sure, somehow, that she found a seat beside Adam, and Lisa envied the easy familiarity that existed between them, but she had also learnt to accept it. It was Willa's display of possessiveness that eventually drew whispered comments from the two women seated on either side of Lisa.

'She can't keep her hands off him, but I don't blame her either,' Molly Anstey remarked a little cynically, nudging Lisa with her elbow.

'Don't take any notice of that girl's behaviour, my dear,' Lisa's mother advised, patting Lisa's arm in a consoling manner.

'It's none of our business, Mother,' Lisa whispered back fiercely, 'and it doesn't interest me in the least.'

'Yes, of course, dear,' Celia Moreau agreed placidly, applying herself to her food once more, but Lisa had the feeling that her mother remained unconvinced on this occasion.

Across the tables laden with food, Lisa saw Willa slide a possessive hand up Adam's arm and, as he looked down at her and smiled, Lisa's stomach lurched sickeningly. Jealousy, as she was beginning to know it, consumed her like a fire, and she lowered her eyes blindly, fighting desperately to control the tremors that shook through her body.

'You're not eating, dear,' Celia Moreau remarked with

concern, and Lisa set aside her plate with a look of distaste on her fine features.

'I'm not hungry.'

Celia looked slightly taken aback, but Lisa had the distinct impression that her mother was hiding a smile behind that fluttering handkerchief.

The *braai* seemed to last an eternity, but when the twins ambled sleepily across to Lisa's chair, she took them up to bed, and rejoiced silently at this temporary escape from the pain of seeing Willa stake her claim so openly.

Laughter and music greeted Lisa when she eventually joined everyone in the garden again, and she was faintly surprised when Willa deliberately sought out her company.

'You will be leaving us soon,' Willa began, drawing Lisa a little away from the rowdy circle of people.

'I'll be leaving in just over two weeks, to be exact,' Lisa replied stiffly.

'Are you looking forward to returning to the city?'

Green eyes surveyed Lisa intently, placing her instantly on her guard. 'I'm looking forward to going back to teaching, yes.'

'Yes, of course,' Willa smiled with deceptive sweetness. 'I'd forgotten you're a teacher, and that reminds me that the twins will soon be attending boarding school. The moment they're off Adam's hands ...' She paused significantly and glanced at Lisa. 'Well, you know what I mean.'

'Yes ... I know,' Lisa spoke with difficulty and, to her dismay, the faint quiver of her lips did not go unnoticed.

'I did warn you not to go silly over him,' Willa thrust the knife home with an accuracy that made Lisa wince inwardly, but she recovered herself swiftly and met Willa's mocking glance with a calmness she had thought had deserted her.

'You did warn me, Willa, and please believe me when I

say that—that I hope you'll both be very happy.'

Incredulity flashed across the other girl's face. 'I believe you really mean that.'

Lisa nodded, her throat too tight to speak at that moment.

'You care for him so much you can wish him happiness with someone else?' Willa persisted, her perfectly arched eyebrows rising a fraction higher. 'I must admit I never thought much of you before, but you certainly have my admiration for your unselfish attitude.'

'Think nothing of it,' Lisa replied through clenched teeth and, turning on her heel, she walked blindly towards the house.

It no longer mattered that Willa knew of her feelings for Adam, and her only thought at that moment was to get away. She had to be alone for a few minutes to rid herself of this deadly coldness that had taken such complete possession of her.

'Just a minute,' a harsh voice commanded, and strong fingers latched on to her arm, bringing her to an abrupt stop in the hall. 'Where are you going?'

'I—I was going up to my—my room for a few minutes,' she explained haltingly, trying to free herself, but Adam's keen glance raked her white face, and his hand tightened on her arm.

'Is something wrong? Has anyone upset you?'

'No ... oh, no! Everything's fine, and——'

'You're shaking,' he interrupted, taking her by the shoulders a little roughly. 'Are you ill?'

'N-no,' she assured him hastily, but she could not stop her teeth from chattering.

'Come with me,' Adam instructed abruptly and, not waiting for her to follow him, he steered her firmly down the passage towards his study, switching on the desk lamp and closing the door behind them.

He regarded her closely for a moment, then he took her shaking hands in his and held them against his chest. 'Your hands are like ice.'

His touch was unbearably sweet, but she dared not linger there alone with him; not while she was in this totally vulnerable state of mind and body.

'I—I must go,' she stammered, but as she looked up into his compelling eyes, something stilled inside of her. She had never seen him look so strained before, nor so strangely white about the mouth.

'Lisa, Lisa,' he muttered thickly, and then those powerful arms were crushing her against him, and his lips sought hers in a kiss that left her peculiarly drained. 'My God, the more I have of you, the more I want,' he growled eventually against her lips, and then he was kissing her again until her bones seemed to melt against him. 'I can't let you go, Lisa. My life would never be the same again without you to add that odd and mysterious dash of spice to it.'

Her heart reacted deliriously to what he was saying, and a new warmth flowed through her, but her wary, tortured mind warned her to take care. 'Adam, you don't know what you're saying.'

'I know damn well what I'm saying, you little witch,' he grunted, the leaping flames in his eyes devouring her. 'I don't know how you did it, but it's a darned uncomfortable feeling for a man like myself when a woman gets under his skin. I haven't known myself lately, and the desire to hold you in my arms like this became unbearable at times. I even found myself trying to create situations which would inevitably lead to this.'

'Adam ...' she interrupted weakly, but he would not be checked.

'I know you're not totally indifferent to me, but, God

help me, I'll make you care somehow.'

'Adam ...' His lips silenced hers, but she clung resolutely to her sanity, and when he finally raised his head, she gasped, 'Adam, you're not yourself. You're——'

'You're quite right, I'm not myself,' he thundered at her angrily. 'I haven't been quite myself since you walked into my life and shook my carefully erected foundations.'

It all sounded ecstatically wonderful, but she had to think of Willa and, leaning back in his arms as far as she could, she looked a long way up into his angry face. 'You don't really mean what you're saying. You've forgotten, perhaps, that you once told me you tolerated me in your home only for the sake of the twins.'

His arms tightened about her painfully. 'Have you forgotten what prompted that remark?'

Lisa shook her head. 'I know I was angry and hurt at the time.'

'You said I was the most hateful man you'd ever met,' he refreshed her memory, and Lisa winced.

'I didn't really mean that.'

'Neither did I mean what I said.' His lips brushed against her cheek. 'Marry me, Lisa.'

'No!' she cried in anguish, straining away from him. 'No, I can't!'

'Why not?'

'I—I'm not the right sort of wife for you, and—and you're not really serious,' she argued haltingly, trying to ward him off, but the sensual exploration of his lips against her neck was rapidly wearing down her fragile resistance.

'My patience is wearing thin, Lisa,' he warned thickly, 'and I won't take "no" for an answer.'

She felt the warmth of his hands through the thin silk of her blouse as they moved across her back, pressing her more firmly against the hard length of his body, but she

dared not give in to the emotions that clamoured for an
outlet, and out of sheer desperation she asked: 'What about
Willa?'

'Willa?' His heavy eyebrows came together in a frown.
'What has Willa got to do with us?'

'But she—she——' Lisa faltered nervously. The look on
his face filled her once again with that vague suspicion that
something was wrong, and she shook her head slightly in
an effort to seek clarity. 'I don't understand.'

'Neither do I, so would you mind explaining?'

He released her suddenly, and she stood swaying for a
moment before her hands encountered the desk behind her.
Was it possible that she had misjudged Adam? she wondered, swallowing convulsively as she took in his formidable expression while he waited for her to speak.

'Willa told me that—that you were planning to be—
married as soon as the twins went to school.'

Adam's eyes narrowed to angry slits. 'Did she actually
mention the word marriage?'

'Well, I——' Lisa frowned suddenly, searching her mind
frantically in an effort to recall Willa's exact words. 'No,'
she said at last. 'Now that I come to think of it, she didn't.
She said—she first of all told me that you had—had committed yourself.'

His lips tightened perceptibly. 'And you understood this
to mean marriage?'

'What else could it have meant?' she argued miserably,
the colour coming and going in her cheeks. 'And then, this
evening, she——'

'Yes?' Adam prompted harshly, making her flinch. 'What
did she say this evening?'

'She said you were just waiting for the twins to go to
boarding school so they would be off your hands,' Lisa re-

plied truthfully. 'She didn't add anything to that, but she didn't have to.'

'And you believed her clever insinuations, of course,' Adam accused quietly, his eyes flickering strangely.

'There was no reason for me *not* to believe her, Adam. I've always considered she would be the perfect wife for you. She knows all there is to know about sheep farming, which is a tremendous asset for any man like yourself, and —and she's strong and healthy. Not like——' She faltered, her throat working as her fingers went automatically to her scarred cheek.

'Forget about that!' Adam ordered sharply, removing her hand and brushing his lips against the long scar before he raised his head and looked deep into her eyes. 'I love you, Lisa, and that's something I've never said to any other woman before.' Her heart was beating so fast that she could not speak as his arms encircled her waist. 'Marry me, Lisa. I know I'm expecting rather a lot of you to take on those two scamps who've been placed in my care as well, but you can't refuse me.'

The most incredible happiness surged through her, but after the weeks of hopeless despair, she was wary of it. 'I love Josh and Kate, but what will Willa say?'

'To the devil with Willa!' he exploded with harsh impatience. 'Put me out of my misery, Lisa, and say you'll marry me.'

'Oh, Adam,' she whispered tremulously, burying her face against him, and then her silent tears of capitulation dampened the front of his immaculate blue shirt where the smell of woodsmoke still clung to him.

'Tears, my beloved?' he demanded with a tenderness which she knew was only for her, and then his fingers were beneath her chin, bringing her tear-dampened face out into the open so that he could read the truth in her luminous, deep blue eyes. 'Does that mean the answer is "yes"?'

'Oh, yes ... yes, Adam ... please,' she sighed ecstatically, and then everything seemed to fade into the distance, leaving only Adam and herself, and the unbelievable joy of knowing she belonged.

She remembered only vaguely afterwards that he had carried her across the room to cradle her on his lap in the old padded armchair, and then he was kissing her gently, tenderly, but with a growing passion that demanded and found a willing response in her.

The bruising strength of his arms was a pleasurable agony she endured in silence until the deliberate sensuality of his hands on her body made her tremble with the storm of emotions that he aroused in her. She felt his heart thudding against her own, and when his lips finally sought the sensitive hollow of her throat she pushed her fingers through his hair and pressed her lips against the greyness at his temples as she had longed to do so often.

They were both in the grip of that sweet madness they had known once before, but neither of them made any effort now to hide what was in their hearts. She saw the leaping flames of desire in his eyes as his fingers fumbled with the tiny buttons of her blouse, and she felt her own desire mounting to match his when his hand gently clasped the soft fullness of her breast, then, with the confidence his love had given her, she drew his head down to hers once more and sought his mouth hungrily with her own.

'My God, I want you,' he groaned after a time, and then, with a supreme effort she had to admire, he controlled himself, and simply held her against him as if he never wanted to let her go.

'Adam ...' she said after a time when sanity had returned and she was able to think coherently again. 'About Willa.'

'Willa has always been a good friend and neighbour, and nothing more,' he replied, fingering a silky curl that was tinted gold in the light of the desk lamp. 'I've certainly never committed myself to her in any way, by word or deed.' He raised her face from its hiding place against his shoulder so that he could look into her eyes. 'Do you believe me?'

'I believe you.'

He kissed her warm lips until they quivered responsively beneath his, then he lifted her on to her feet and stood up. 'Lisa my darling, I hate the thought of sharing you with everyone else just yet, but we'd better put in an appearance and inform our guests that this is no longer just a farewell *braai* for your mother and your aunt, but also an engagement celebration.'

'Adam, wait!' she pleaded, escaping from his arms to restore a little order to her appearance. 'You're going much too fast for me, and I would like to prepare my mother for this before you make such an announcement.'

'Your mother has been prepared for this since before her arrival.'

'What do you mean?'

He smiled down into her bewildered eyes with tolerant amusement as he took her hands in his and drew her relentlessly towards him. 'I mean, my little one, that I not only wrote and asked her to spend Christmas with us, but I also made my intentions quite clear.'

Lisa's expression became incredulous. 'You mean she's known all this time?'

'Yes,' Adam admitted. 'She gave me her blessing soon after her arrival here on the farm, and promised to try and find out if there was any hope for me, but both your mother and your aunt told me that you either became evasive, or shut up like a clam whenever they mentioned my name.'

His eyes clouded, and his arms went around her almost convulsively. 'I've had some pretty anxious moments because of you, my darling, but I realise now, of course, why I could never get through to you before.'

'I thought you were just amusing yourself with me,' she whispered, an impish smile curving her lips as she leaned against him. 'I considered you an absolute rake.'

'A rake, am I?' he demanded with a harshness that no longer frightened her, then his lips took possession of hers in a punishing yet oddly sensual way that raised havoc with her emotions.

'When will you marry me?' he demanded after a considerable time had elapsed, and that square, resolute chin jutted out firmly. 'I might as well warn you, Lisa, that I have no intention of waiting several months. I want us to be married as soon as possible.'

'But Adam——'

'No arguments!' he silenced her, then his glance grew a little wary. 'I suppose you want a white wedding with all the paraphernalia that goes with it?'

'Not particularly, Adam. Not if you don't want that,' she assured him gently, fingering the cleft in his chin and tentatively tracing the outline of the mouth she had once thought so harsh and unrelenting. 'I would like to wear white, though,' she added, 'but nothing elaborate, and I would prefer it to be a quiet wedding.'

'That suits me,' he sighed with obvious relief as he caught her hand and pressed his warm lips into her palm. 'When?'

The banked-down fire in the eyes that regarded her so steadily sent a now familiar weakness surging into her limbs, and there was a tremor in her voice when she said: 'I'm beginning to realise it will have to be soon.'

'A week from today?'

'As soon as that?' she asked, a little taken aback.

'If you want to wear white, yes,' he warned, his warm glance sliding over her.

'Oh, Adam,' she laughed unsteadily, hiding her hot face against him, but Adam would have none of that.

'You look adorable when you blush,' he teased her softly, forcing her face out into the open and, forgetting her embarrassment momentarily, she marvelled at the change in his harshly chiselled features. There was tenderness in every line and angle of his face, and the wonder was that she had put it there.

'I love you, Adam,' she whispered impulsively but truthfully, her eyes darkening with the emotions that were pulsing through her. 'I love you so very much.'

His chest heaved beneath her hands, and then she was crushed against him with a fierceness that was both an agony and a pleasure.

'You're going to have to put up with a lot of loving from me,' he warned, his voice vibrating with emotion. 'Do you think you'll be able to take it?'

'I'll manage, I think,' she smiled dreamily, drawing his head down to hers until their lips met in a long, satisfying kiss.

Lisa felt as if she was walking on air when they finally left the study, but as they walked out on to the verandah she drew back nervously.

'Adam . . .' She bit her lip as she glanced up at him. 'Must you make the announcement now?'

'The sooner the better,' he said adamantly, placing a protective arm about her and drawing her towards the circle of people seated about the fire. 'May I have your attention, please?' he began, and the conversation ceased abruptly. Lisa was unaware of the curious glances directed at them as she glimpsed the cold, hard suspicion that began to glimmer in the green depths of Willa's eyes moments before Adam said: 'I'd like you all to know that Lisa has just consented to become my wife.'

Pandemonium seemed to break loose after Adam's announcement, and Willa was obscured from Lisa's vision as she and Adam became separated by the exuberance of the well-wishers. Her mother was tearful but happy, Aunt Molly was positively gloating that her suspicions had been confirmed, and Erica Vandeleur gathered Lisa into her arms and declared openly that she could not have chosen a better wife for her impossible son.

Willa and Lisa finally came face to face, but, to Lisa's relief, there was no sign of malice on the other girl's controlled features as she graciously admitted defeat.

'You've won, Lisa,' she smiled faintly. 'No hard feelings, I hope?'

'Of course not,' Lisa assured her hastily and, despite the heartache Willa had caused her, she could not help feeling sorry for her, but there was no time to say more as Ken Rudman drew her aside.

'I was wrong about the boss, but I guessed right about you, didn't I?' he teased lightly, and when she nodded silently, he grimaced slightly through his boyish smile. 'I can't help wishing it was me, but congratulations all the same.'

He leaned forward and planted a kiss firmly on her lips just as Adam came up behind them. 'That will do, Rudman.'

There was no sign of anger in Adam's command, but the arm he placed about Lisa was faintly possessive, and Ken grinned a little crookedly as he shook hands with Adam.

Adam did not believe in wasting time, and it took him barely a few seconds to persuade Lisa's mother and her aunt to postpone their departure for a week until after the wedding. Then he brought out several bottles of champagne from somewhere and, with everyone's glasses filled, Erica Vandeleur suggested proudly that they drink a toast to Adam and Lisa's future happiness.

When the glasses had been filled a second time, Adam came to Lisa's side where she stood behind her mother's chair and, when no one was looking, he slipped his arm about her waist.

'Come this way,' he whispered in her ear, drawing her away from the others.

'Adam ...' she whispered back urgently when they reached the trees, 'where are you taking me?'

'Hush!' he ordered softly, then she was lifted in his arms and carried swiftly and effortlessly deeper into the shadows before she was placed on her feet again. 'I've got something for you. I intended it to be your Christmas present, but you were so cold and aloof at the time that it had to wait.'

'What is it?' she asked curiously as he extracted something from the pocket of his pants.

'An engagement ring.'

'Oh, Adam,' she exclaimed softly as he took her hand in his and slipped the ring on to her finger. 'I wish it wasn't so dark here beneath the trees.'

'You can look at it later,' he ordered, covering the ring with his hand and drawing her into his arms. 'Right now there are more urgent matters to attend to.'

'Such as?' she teased, but already her senses were responding wildly to his nearness and his touch.

'Such as *you* convincing *me* that I'm not just dreaming,' he announced hoarsely, his face a dark blur in the shadows.

'Adam ... darling,' she murmured unsteadily, and the stars settled in her eyes as she raised her lips to his.

The night went silent about them as they kissed, and kissed again with a hunger that could not be assuaged.

There was so much still to discuss, and so much she still wanted to say, but for now there was only the incredible wonder that Adam loved her and needed her. Her loneliness and despair was something of the past, and her cup of happiness was filled to the brim.

And things can never go badly wrong
If the heart be true and the love be strong,
For the mist, if it comes, and the weeping rain
Will be changed by the love into sunshine again.

Harlequin Romances

The books that let you escape
into the wonderful world of romance!
Trips to exotic places...interesting
plots...meeting memorable people...
the excitement of love....These are
integral parts of Harlequin Romances—
the heartwarming novels read by
women everywhere.

Many early issues are now available.
Choose from this great selection!

Choose from this list of Harlequin Romance editions.*

422 **Then Come Kiss Me**
Mary Burchell

434 **Dear Doctor Everett**
Jean S. MacLeod

459 **Second Love**
(Ring for the Nurse)
Marjorie Moore

481 **Bachelor of Medicine**
Alex Stuart

492 **Follow a Dream**
(Hospital Pro)
Marjorie Moore

508 **Senior Surgeon**
Marjorie Moore

509 **A Year to Remember**
(Nurse Secretary)
Marjorie Moore

517 **Journey in the Sun**
(Doctors Together)
Jean S. MacLeod

535 **Under the Red Cross**
Juliet Shore

559 **The Time of Enchantment**
(Nurse Wayne in the Tropics)
Anne Vinton

583 **This Merry Bond**
Sara Seale

634 **Love without Wings**
(Surgeon's Wife)
Margaret Malcolm

636 **The Home at Hawk's Nest**
(Nurse Candida)
Caroline Trench

673 **Gateway to Happiness**
(Village Clinic)
Ann Cameron

683 **Desire for the Star**
(Doctor's Desire)
Averil Ives

684 **Doctor on Horseback**
Alex Stuart

713 **Harvest of the Heart**
(Nurse of My Heart)
Jill Christian

714 **Conduct Unbecoming**
(Young Nurse Payne)
Valerie K. Nelson

729 **One with the Wind**
(Surgeons at Arms)
Mary Hunton

737 **Maiden Flight**
Betty Beaty

746 **Loyal in All**
(Nurse Marika, Loyal in All)
Mary Burchell

748 **The Valley of Palms**
Jean S. MacLeod

798 **If This Is Love**
Anne Weale

799 **Love Is for Ever**
Barbara Rowan

810 **The Piper of Laide**
(Doctor of Rhua)
Alex Stuart

815 **Young Tracy**
Rosalind Brett

838 **Dear Dragon**
Sara Seale

872 **Haven of the Heart**
Averil Ives

878 **The Dangerous Kind of Love**
(This Kind of Love)
Kathryn Blair

888 **Heart of a Rose**
Rachel Lindsay

902 **Mountain of Dreams**
Barbara Rowen

903 **So Loved and So Far**
Elizabeth Hoy

909 **Desert Doorway**
Pamela Kent

920 **The Man at Mulera**
Kathryn Blair

927 **The Scars Shall Fade**
Nerina Hilliard

941 **Mayenga Farm**
Kathryn Blair

*Some of these book were originally published under different titles.

Relive a great love story...
with Harlequin Romances
Complete and mail this coupon today!

Harlequin Reader Service

In U.S.A.
MPO Box 707
Niagara Falls, N.Y. 14302

In Canada
649 Ontario St.
Stratford, Ontario, N5A 6W2

Please send me the following Harlequin Romance novels. I am enclosing my check or money order for $1.25 for each novel ordered, plus 59¢ to cover postage and handling.

☐ 422	☐ 509	☐ 636	☐ 729	☐ 810	☐ 902
☐ 434	☐ 517	☐ 673	☐ 737	☐ 815	☐ 903
☐ 459	☐ 535	☐ 683	☐ 746	☐ 838	☐ 909
☐ 481	☐ 559	☐ 684	☐ 748	☐ 872	☐ 920
☐ 492	☐ 583	☐ 713	☐ 798	☐ 878	☐ 927
☐ 508	☐ 634	☐ 714	☐ 799	☐ 888	☐ 941

Number of novels checked @ $1.25 each = $ _____

N.Y. and Ariz. residents add appropriate sales tax. $ _____

Postage and handling $ _____ .59

TOTAL $ _____

I enclose _____
(Please send check or money order. We cannot be responsible for cash sent through the mail.)

Prices subject to change without notice.

NAME _____
(Please Print)

ADDRESS _____

CITY _____

STATE/PROV. _____

ZIP/POSTAL CODE _____

Offer expires December 31, 1981.

104563371